Our

Glad

Our Glad

by Joyce Warren

Harper & Brothers  New York

OUR GLAD

Copyright © 1957 by Joyce Warren
Printed in the United States of America

All rights in this book are reserved.
No part of the book may be used or reproduced in any manner whatsoever without written permission except in the case of brief quotations embodied in critical articles and reviews. For information address Harper & Brothers
49 East 33rd Street, New York 16, N. Y.

"Daddy Wouldn't Buy Me a Bow-Wow, Bow-Wow": Copyright 1892 by Francis, Day & Hunter, Ltd. and reprinted by permission

for
     Charles R. Warren

Acknowledgments

I should like to express my thanks to the trustees of The Eugene F. Saxton Memorial Trust for a grant which enabled me to spend a summer in England collecting material for this book. I also received invaluable help from Miss Maria Garde, Mr. Reginald Vincent, and Mr. Christopher Pulling.

I am grateful to Messrs. Reynolds & Co. of London who through Mr. V. F. Stevens gave me free access to and use of their publications. The following Reynolds' properties have been used or quoted from: *Flappers*, by Con West; *My Beastly Eyeglass* and *Really? Yes —Great Scott!* by Harold Montague; *Business as Usual*, by Robert Rutherford; *On Gardening*, by V. F. Stevens; two pantomimes, *The Sleeping Beauty* and *Queen of Hearts*, both by Fred Rome; and *My Old Dutch*, which I believe was written by Albert Chevalier. I have also consulted *They Were Singing*, by Christopher Pulling, published in 1952 by George G. Harrap & Co., and Mr. Sigmund Spaeth's two books, *Read 'Em and Weep* and *Weep Some More, My Lady*, published by Doubleday Page in 1926 and 1927 respectively. Messrs. Cassell & Co., Ltd., have given permission to quote parts of *Dumb, Dumb, Dumb; Early One Morning;* and *The Rosebud*, published by them in *The Gaudeamus Song Book* edited by John Farmer in 1892. *Daddy Wouldn't Buy Me a Bow-Wow, Bow-Wow*, copyright 1892 by Francis, Day & Hunter, Ltd., is also reprinted by permission.

It has been impossible to trace the copyright holders of all the songs quoted. If anyone has been overlooked, I hope he will accept my apologies and thanks.

As for the characters mentioned in the story, they could have existed, but to the best of my knowledge they are fictitious.

J. W.

Part I

1

WHEN the women of Tor, Derbyshire, tell their children not to wander far from the gibbet, they mean exactly what they say. The gibbet stands in the center of the village green, and the women of the cottages around the green keep an eye on all the children playing there—their own and everyone else's. The gibbet is, of course, no longer used for its original purpose. In fact, the framework has long since weathered away, and all that remains is a square stone platform with flights of steps leading up to it from the four sides, and with two big stones, one above the other, in the middle. The uppermost stone is hollowed out to form a bird bath, but otherwise the platform is much as it has always been.

Keeping the gibbet bird bath filled is no problem, for Tor lies on the rainy side of the Derbyshire Peak. This means that for most of the year the weather is gray and overcast, and even on those few summer days when the sun does occasionally shine, there is usually some rain before nightfall. People who come to Tor from other parts of England find the neighborhood depressing—you have to be born there, or go to live there while you are still a small child, really to appreciate it. But according to Derbyshire folk, the idea that gray, misty weather and rain-laden winds make a person feel gloomy is an invention of foreigners. The people of Tor like their weather, or, if they do not, they accept it as they accept their neighbors—not necessarily what one might choose, but what one has.

Although the center of life for the children of Tor has for centuries been the gibbet, the social center for the adult population in 1911 was The Nag's Head Inn, owned and operated by Fred Miller, the husband of Holly Miller, and the father of Gladys, Blanche, Lily, Edith and Flo.

Fred Miller was the son of a Tor farmer. He'd been sickly as a child, and had never grown strong enough to farm, so at sixteen he'd hired himself out as a bartender. In due course, he married the innkeeper's daughter, and later he inherited the inn. He was a tall, thin man with dark hair, a long nose and a quiet, sympathetic manner. Like a good many reserved people, he was stubborn, passionate and slow-thinking. Holly was twenty-five when she married Fred because it took her four and a half years to convince him that he was in love.

The Nag's Head, like most village inns in England, combined the functions of a club, a social center, a restaurant and a psychiatrist's consulting room. More than any other single institution, it set the tone of the village, established codes of behavior and saw to it that these were observed. For a man to be refused the right of entry to The Nag's Head bar because of some misdemeanor was an ostracism none could withstand for long. The bar, like the Judgment Seat, might be a place where one suffered from being too well known, but the anonymity of the world outside was worse. In The Nag's Head, one heard the news and talked it over, one helped nominate the members of the cricket team, one discussed, or heard discussed, the sale or purchase of pigeons, rabbits and racing dogs. In addition, games were played. The Nag's Head owned a dartboard and a skittle alley, but the favorite game was one exclusively its own —the Ring and the Bull. In this game, one swung a ring, which was attached by a string to the ceiling, in such a way that it hooked itself on the horn of a bull's head that jutted out from the wall.

Most English villages have more than one inn, and each has its own clientele, but there is always one house that becomes the forum for local opinion and politics. Which inn this is does not depend, as one might think, upon the quality of the beer dispensed or even upon the geographical location of the place. In Wrangle, for instance, scarcely anybody goes to The Trout, a charming inn right near the rowboat rental dock that has to depend for its custom on holiday traffic. Instead, people make for The Young Vanish, a stiff quarter-mile climb from the main road. Munby is much the same, and so is Eye. What settles the choice is the personality of the innkeeper, though of course the beer has to be good too and the barmaid pretty. All innkeepers are tolerant, reliable men, but some encourage confidences, others do not. The innkeepers who succeed are mostly those who are more interested in how a man is than in how much beer he buys, with the result that the customer probably stays longer than he intended to and buys more beer anyway, bringing his friends with him next time to do the same. Thus in Tor, with The Midge Inn on the green and The Old Spot in the valley, most people gravitated to The Nag's Head, halfway down the hillside.

From the atmosphere of the bar, one might think that it was Holly rather than Fred who ran the inn. Born in the same brass bedstead in the upstairs front room where, later, she produced her own five daughters, Holly was, naturally enough, completely at home in The Nag's Head. She was a cheerful, rather noisy woman, who, in spite of her children, had never really lost her baby chubbiness, but she had no head at all for business—the inn was entirely Fred's. He kept the books and paid the bills and ordered the supplies, while Holly chose the barmaids and sent them to Fred to discuss money. Fred listened to the troubles of the sad customers and Holly exchanged jokes with the happy ones. Fred decided who could be allowed to pay later, but it was Holly who, on those rare occasions when the bar grew rough, decided who was to be ordered home, and herself did the ordering. It says much for the high regard in which the village held the Millers that invariably, after such an event, a formal apology (made to Fred, as the owner of the inn) was forthcoming the next day.

The Nag's Head was run with shining precision—never a speck of dust or a glass out of its place. But back in the house where the family lived, the housekeeping was considerably more vague. Holly washed and cleaned when she felt in the mood, and no child was ever expected to put her belongings away. Christmas decorations hung on and on into the late spring, and all summer long there were damp swimsuits and sneakers cluttering up the hall.

In Holly's defense, it must be said that The Nag's Head was not an easy house to look after. The living quarters were not large enough for seven people, especially when six of the seven were women. Parts of the inn dated from the thirteenth century (the Ring and the Bull was said to have been played there since Edward II's reign) and there were only three bedrooms, one of which had to be kept free for overnight guests—usually commercial travelers. The bedroom shared by the five little girls had originally been a brewing room. This meant that it was dark and, since the inn itself was built into the side of a cliff, bedrock showed through the plaster in places. The floors were uneven and there were little staircases everywhere, even a step or two between the rooms. It was the only house in Tor that had closets—cupboards hollowed out of the rock—in which, if one did not hang it up carefully, a child's dress might disappear altogether down a crack in the rock below. The kitchen was immediately back of the bar, and here the wooden leaves of the big table, which extended a foot or so beyond their base all around, could be removed to expose a bathtub large enough to contain all Fred Miller's progeny at one time. The house was damp—often the walls streamed with water—and in such surroundings it was a miracle that the family remained healthy, but Fred, the only one not born in the house, was the only one subject to colds. Holly believed the children's robustness to be due to beer: they were fed ale the way most children are fed cow's milk, and the old walls of their home had of course been absorbing the smell of the stuff for centuries.

Holly was an excellent, though somewhat slapdash mother. There was always an ample supply around the inn of good food, warm clothes, affection and laughter, and in this atmosphere the little Millers flourished like a nest of fledglings, which is hardly surprising since they received much the same kind of care.

Although the inn kept him busy, Fred Miller had time for three hobbies: he gardened, he bred rabbits and he sang. The inn garden was built on terraces down the hill below the house, and here Fred grew enough vegetables to supply Holly with most of what she needed. The Nag's Head had no separate restaurant, but all year round meat pie and cheese could be bought at the counter, supplemented by vegetable soup, apples, fresh celery or whatever Fred happened to have ready at the time.

The rabbits occupied half a dozen hutches at one side of the inn yard. Although Fred spent many hours peering happily through the wire-netting windows at the small, harassed faces peering out, he was not at all sentimental about his pets. He killed a couple for dinner whenever Holly asked him to, and now and again he sold some for their fur. The children were not allowed to touch their father's animals, but they had rabbits of their own in another part of the yard—great, overfed creatures that spent most of their time padding heavily about on the loose, and stamping angrily if their requirements were not immediately attended to.

Fred's gardening and rabbit breeding were his solitary amusements; his singing all the family shared. Fred had a thin tenor voice and he was a charter member of the Tor and New Cut Glee Club.

The little Millers grew up accustomed to a good deal of singing going on around the house, for Fred was supposed to practice and Holly liked to help him. There was an old upright Chappell piano in the bar, and, although its constant use by inexpert customers had not improved its tone, Holly was able to beat out most of Fred's accompaniments. What she could not play, she sang, and the whole business would usually end in shouts of laughter, with Fred and Holly kissing on the piano stool, and Fred knowing no more of his part for the next glee club rehearsal than he had known when he left the last one.

The five Miller daughters, spaced two years apart in age, were an unusually amicable group. Gladys, born at the turn of the century, was the eldest. At eleven years old, she was tall for her age and very thin, with straight black hair and her father's long nose. She was not at all a pretty child, but she made up for her lack of looks by a tremendous vitality. Gladys sincerely enjoyed everything that happened to her ("Well, this *is* nice, Mum. Saturday afternoon, and me with absolutely nothing to do!"). Her sister Blanche, a chubby little blonde, was already, at the age of nine, devout. Lily, thin and dark like Gladys, came next; then Edith, blonde and fat like Blanche, and finally Flo, the baby and the beauty of the family, the only one to inherit Holly's round, sweet face.

The Domesday Book describes Tor as a farming community, and so it was until, toward the end of the last century, coal was found in the valley. This made a considerable difference to the financial outlook of most of the families in Tor, who had, until then, known no alternative to the profession of their fathers. The young men of the old villages in the district thought the dangers and the long hours of work underground well balanced by the fat pay envelopes, and it was not long before some of the cottage homes found themselves with more than one breadwinner in the family. In 1911, a man was considered old enough to work by the time he reached the age of twelve.

With several incomes in the family, and each larger than the previous farming income, the men of Tor found themselves in unaccustomed prosperity, and the advent of the coal mine brought a general improvement in trade. The miners spent a large part of the extra money they earned on entertaining their wives. More and more of them brought their womenfolk with them when they came to the inn of an evening, and there was, in consequence, an increase in the consumption of the better wines. While the wives gossiped over their port, the men took each other on at darts or the Ring and the Bull, and it became the thing to finish off an evening, several couples together, with a round of cherry brandy rather than bitter or mild.

Thus, naturally enough, the first places to feel the new prosperity were The Midge, The Old Spot and The Nag's Head. There was not, however, an increase in drunkenness. Derbyshire folk are not heavy drinkers. In the case of the one known toper, Holly would say, "That will be all for tonight, Mr. Winters," in a voice firm enough to ensure obedience and yet gentle enough so that the old man's wavering pride was not hurt. And if anyone needed help in negotiating the door or the road home at closing time, Holly did not see him if she could help it—she had a highly developed respect for the dignity of The Nag's Head's customers.

Fred, being a prudent man, used his extra income to make capital improvements. He pulled down one of the old stables and extended the inn yard, thus making more room for the annual pet show, a spring activity. He planted grass in part of the vegetable garden and engaged Tolman, the carpenter, to make tables and chairs that could remain outdoors in all weathers, and he built a rock garden out of the low tumble-down stone fence at the far end of his property. These projects took a great deal of time and discussion, and they put a stop to the loose talk Fred had overheard that the pet show might do well to move to a field in the valley where there was more space and where, incidentally, it would be as handy for strangers to the village to refresh themselves at The Old Spot.

Next, Fred insured his life. A big insurance company of Manley, the nearest market town, had recently opened a branch office in Tor, with a representative to sell policies and collect premiums. Holly, who had been greatly in favor of pulling down the stable and making the rock garden, was dead against the insurance. She could not see the need, anyway not yet, and she did not trust Mr. Murphy, the local representative, whom she knew as a teetotaler always in and out of different jobs. Fred, however, took the policy out anyway and ignored the tone of his wife's voice when she called to

Part I 9

him, on the first Saturday afternoon of each month: "Your friend Murphy's here for his pay again."

Once having expressed her opinion on a subject, however, Holly did not nag. Fred was thinking gratefully of this on the first Saturday afternoon of August, 1911, as he sat in the big bathtub in the kitchen, while Holly scrubbed his back. Mr. Murphy, burdened with a frightful cold, had called half an hour before, and Holly, having made her usual comment, was now cheerfully singing. She is a very good wife to me, Fred thought: I should like to buy her a present.

This notion, which sprang into Fred's mind light as a feather, was destined to change the lives of the entire Miller clan. Fred realized at the time that his idea was unusual, for he had only made two gifts to Holly in his life—a small pearl ring when they became engaged, and a broad gold band when they married.

Some families are always giving each other presents—at Christmas, on birthdays, for Easter, on St. Valentine's Day, and whenever anyone loses a tooth. The Millers, who could hardly have been a more devoted family, never gave each other presents at all. On Christmas Eve, each child hung up her sock, and Holly filled these with apples and oranges, nuts and candy. On birthdays, there was a party and a cake, with, perhaps, a family visit to the fair. But the business of formal present-giving, with all the list-making, shopping, wrapping up and unwrapping that this entails, would have seemed silly to the Millers. The little girls, who always quickly smashed or broke any presents that *did* come their way, thought of celebrations solely in terms of food: a birthday was a day like any other except that it contained larger, longer and more exciting meals.

It was therefore beyond Fred's powers of imagination to choose a present for Holly. Indeed, he hardly knew how to put it to her that she was to have one. She was rubbing the hard towel over his shoulder blades when he made the announcement—loudly, and in an abrupt voice.

Holly was stunned. "For *me*? Oh, Fred! How much?"

He was in for it now—no holds. "Anything tha likes," he said. "No limit."

Holly dropped the towel and clung to him. His legs were still wet. She knew exactly what she wanted. "I ain't been to the beach for thirteen years," she said. "I'd like to go one of those day trips to Skunby-on-Sea. Not the kids—just us."

2

TOR is built on the south edge of a flattish upland in the Peak district. The Norman church, the rectory and the big house, Leake Revel, stand back of the green to the north and slightly above it. The two-room schoolhouse lies on the west side of the green. Behind the cottages on the east and west sides of the green are several farms. To the south, the land drops sharply away into a narrow valley, spilling little cottages over the hillside. Pathways, some so steep that they have steps cut in them, wind in and out among the houses, and a road zigzags as far as The Nag's Head, under the cliff halfway down, before taking off eastward in the direction of Manley. Along the floor of the valley runs the River Thorne, a small stream which, luckily for Tor children, contains several fine swimming holes.

Tor, like its weather, is gray. The church, the farms and most of the houses are built of gray stone, and are either roofed with gray-blue slate or thatched. The road past The Nag's Head is surfaced with gray gravel, and if one takes any of the little staircase footpaths, one steadies oneself by grayed wooden railings. The fields surrounding the village are separated from each other by gray stone walls, and beyond them the purplish gray moor stretches away into the distance until it becomes lost in gray mist and low-lying gray cloud. Even the new buildings, the red brick ones constructed during the last hundred years, are rapidly graying over, due to the deposits of soot that are dropped upon them by the smokestacks of Halesowen colliery.

The Halesowen Company sank their coal mine two miles down the valley from Tor, on land bought from the Leake family. Beyond the mine, they cut back some of the steep hillside to make room for a village which for this reason was called New Cut. New Cut consists of six hundred identical houses set in eight rows facing each other in pairs. The houses look like so many bumps on a bar of cooking chocolate, and since they are thoroughly coated with

Part I

soot—New Cut's position, east of the colliery, is down the prevailing wind—they seem even more forbidding than the cottages at Tor. Nobody, however, minds this. The New Cut houses are roomy and stoutly built, and although, in 1911, they lacked plumbing, the nominal rent included light and as much coal as a householder could want.

When New Cut was built, miners from other parts of Derbyshire moved in. At first, the natives of Tor were suspicious of the strangers, but they soon warmed to them when they discovered that the Halesowen Company had more jobs to offer than the residents of New Cut could handle, and there was work for anyone who cared to apply for it. In one way or another, everybody benefited, including the Leake family, who were the former owners of the colliery lands and who received royalties on every ton of coal mined from beneath their property.

The Leakes (they pronounced their name "Lake"), lived at Leake Revel, the largest house in Tor. Leake Revel was an Elizabethan manor with eighteen bedrooms. It lay northeast of the village at the top of the ridge, and it dominated the surrounding countryside as well as the Leake family. The front of the house was three stories high. Several of the large windows had been bricked up to save paying window tax in 1697. These bricked-up windows gave the house a curiously unkempt appearance, for the blocking had been done from the inside, leaving the original glass in position, and it looked as if Lady Leake only kept certain windows washed. During Victorian times, a two-story wing of bedrooms had been added to the back of the house. Beyond this lay the stables and a paved courtyard. The large garden was surrounded by a high, prisonlike, stone wall.

Leake Revel was a house with character; it was noisy, full of creaks and grumblings and, like an elderly person no longer able to keep track of his belongings, it frequently mislaid slates, rain spouts, pieces of cement or plaster or, during a storm, a chimney pot or two. Keeping the place patched up and, as it were, on its feet, was a continuous expense to its owners.

The Leakes were an army family. Generations of warriors had been nurtured within Leake Revel's thick, damp walls, though in 1911 only women lived there. Lady Leake, the widow of the late Sir James, was the mother of three children, two girls and a boy.

Jamie Leake, the youngest, had tuberculosis, and because of this he spent the first twenty years of his life in Switzerland.

Six servants were required to run Leake Revel, but even as early in the century as 1911, Lady Leake had difficulty in keeping a staff together. The old house seemed to take particular pleasure in frightening maids, by making their first days in the place as eerie as possible. The village girls, who knew the house and might have been expected to enjoy a job near home, refused to come for that reason—they wanted to work where it was possible to see an end to the day's chores. Servants imported from London, Ireland or France (Lady Leake tried everything) rarely stayed more than a few hours. After their first cup of tea in Leake Revel's bleak kitchen, with the house complaining around them, many were too scared even to wait until the next morning to leave.

The Leakes adored their ancient home and were undismayed by its foibles. They treated the old place as they might have treated some tiresome relative who had forgotten how to die. Leake Revel was permitted to absorb any amount of the family's money and time, and even, on occasions, their careers, for somebody always had to be on hand to attend to the estate's problems.

Lady Leake's servant difficulties were not helped by the fact that for generations the Leakes had been collectors of foreign loot. Each of the five reception rooms at Leake Revel was crowded with carved chests and inlaid tables, with china, lacquer and glassware, and with little gold clocks that ticked feverishly against one another. The walls were studded with pale prints, Indian fans and Japanese *kakemono*, and the floors were covered with big Persian carpets and treacherously slippery little hand-woven rugs. The entrance hall, which was brightly tiled, showed every speck of dust, and had to be scrubbed daily and mopped over in between times. Most of the bedrooms, sparsely furnished as they were with hard, valuable bedsteads and tall bureaus whose heavy drawers constantly became wedged, were ornamented with trophies of male activity—spears, swords, shields and long, heavy whips.

Margaret and Catherine, Lady Leake's two daughters, were raised to respect and never to touch the *objets de guerre* with which their home was cluttered. In a smaller house, it would have been impossible to enforce such a rule, but the Leake young had their

Part I

own living quarters and these were furnished with nothing children could spoil.

According to her lights, Lady Leake was a devoted mother. She obtained for her daughters the best nurses and governesses available in the narrow field of persons willing to expose themselves to the depressing atmosphere of Tor, and she bought them dogs and ponies and piano lessons. She did not, however, permit them to have any friends. The village children were not considered suitable companions, and there was no one else.

Lady Leake was a tall, pale, bony woman. With one exception, she too lacked friends, though this was entirely her own fault—unfortunately, she was a snob. Her son, her husband's memory, her husband's house and her daughters were her only real interests, and she loved them in that order; her one hope was that Jamie, although he would never be well enough to follow his family into the army, would one day be able to make his home at Leake Revel. Lady Leake did not, however, pity either her son or herself: not for nothing had she married into a family whose motto, exhaustively inscribed wherever stone and ironwork about the place permitted, was *Officio Fungi* (To Do One's Duty). Having enlisted the services of the best doctors she knew to help Jamie, she turned her attention to her duties in the village.

There were many of these. Lady Leake was president of every local organization, she sat on committees, helped at the Baby Welfare Clinic, taught a Bible class and called punctiliously on all who were sick. She tithed her income and she brought her children up to do the same, she attended church, and she listened carefully to the words of the one friend she permitted herself in the neighborhood, the rector of Tor, the Reverend Martin Hay.

Martin Hay was in a way as much a member of the staff of Leake Revel as the domestics there—his living was in Lady Leake's gift. This curious system, which dates from the days when a great house had its own chaplain, still operates in parts of England. Lady Leake's nominations required the approval of the bishop of the diocese, and as a matter of courtesy she gave the Tor churchwardens advance notice of her decisions, but legally the village had no say at all in the calling of its minister. The present incumbent was lame, over forty and a bachelor, and Lady Leake had given him the job for two reasons, both of them bad. Martin Hay had formerly been chaplain to her husband's regiment, and, being a bachelor, he had no wife to point out to him that the rectory, a beautifully proportioned eighteenth-century house, stood within Leake Revel's garden walls full in the view of Lady Leake's drawing-room windows.

It so happened, however, that Martin Hay was the most popular rector Tor remembered. The village liked his direct manner, his short sermons and the fact that he took a serious interest in the things that interested them—in singing, whippet racing, bell ringing, gardening and digging coal. In many ways Martin behaved as if he had been born and bred in the Tor neighborhood. When he came to call, as often as not he sat in silence for the traditional twenty minutes of his stay, and on the day Joe Stanford's new whippet bitch arrived, it was the rector's idea to put choir practice back an hour, so that Joe could get the crate opened and everybody could get a look at her by daylight.

Mrs. Bennett, the rector's housekeeper, felt sure Martin would not stay. He stocked too good a wine cellar and owned too many clothes for a country parson, and he had too much secular literature —only one shelf in his library contained theological works. But Martin did stay. Tor provided him with exactly what he wanted—ample work, undemanding society, and the companionship of people in whom the sight of a lame leg provoked neither interest nor sympathy—mining accidents were more common in those days than they are now. By 1911, Martin Hay had been rector of Tor for ten years, and during a recent visit to The Nag's Head (a good deal of parish business was conducted there, between games of the Ring and the Bull), he had heard it mentioned that the ringers were considering inviting him to take a rope next time they needed an extra hand, provided of course that the change to be rung was not a complicated one. No surer sign of a man's acceptance by the community could be made than that.

3

When Fred Miller made his wife the magnificent offer of a present, he had no idea that she would choose anything as complex as a day by the sea. Fred was the kind of man who sees no sense in eating a meal out when there are perfectly good meals obtainable on the kitchen table at home, and he did not in the least understand vacations. He would not, however, go back on his word, although he was startled enough to say: "Aw, come now, Holly! Skunby-on-Sea ain't reasonable. What about the pub?"

"Rose can manage for once," Holly said. Rose was the barmaid. "And Robbie and Bert and the others'll be glad to help."

"Well, I know, but these trips are on Saturdays, our busiest day, and besides"—this next was a mistake—"we've never *been* away, not since we was married."

"Lordy, Fred! All the more reason. It does folks good to see the world."

Holly's preparations to see the world, or rather a small area of it that lay seventy miles east of The Nag's Head, took several weeks. Before they could go, she found it necessary to clean the inn from top to bottom, repaint the window frames, and lay a new piece of linoleum on the kitchen floor. She had also to wash, iron and mend all the clothes she had, and make two new dresses.

Fred's preparations took half an hour. As Holly had surmised, Rose was very pleased to take charge, and Fred's glee club friends were all ready to help. The village took almost as much interest in the project as Holly did, with the result that Fred began to feel better. Day trips by train to the seaside were common enough by this time, but not to the people of Tor and New Cut, and Fred's venture was looked upon as both enterprising and generous.

Arrangements for taking care of the children were also very easily made. Holly invited Rose and Rose's mother, Mrs. Dutton, to come and spend the night before the Millers' trip and the night after it at the inn. Rose's mother was a widow and even more set in her ways than Fred, so the plan for the old lady and her daughter to spend two nights in a house several yards from their own cottage caused almost as much commotion in the village as the trip to Skunby.

The journey from Tor to Skunby was one that any man might hesitate to make, even a man who wanted to go. The excursion train left Nottingham at 7 A.M., and this meant that Fred and Holly had to leave Tor by the paddy train at five. The paddy was a special train that brought miners to New Cut from the villages along the twenty-five mile line to Nottingham, and it made the trip every eight hours, stopping at all stations. The excursion from Nottingham took two hours for the fifty-mile journey to Skunby, and it returned to Nottingham at midnight. As there were no Sunday paddy trains (the colliery closed for repairs that day) the Millers would have no transportation beyond Manley, and they would have to walk the remaining three miles home.

Fred explained all this to Holly ahead of time, but it did not persuade her to change her mind. This only happened on the morning of their departure, when, in Fred's opinion, they were too deeply committed to do otherwise than go: the Duttons had already moved in, and the children had been kissed good-by, Fred had handed over a spare set of the inn's keys to Bob Greenhaugh, the policeman, and a basket containing sandwiches, apples and seasickness pills stood ready packed in the kitchen. That morning, Holly had lain awake until half-past three, and then she dressed and prepared breakfast. During this meal, she suddenly burst into tears and told Fred she could not go. She could not possibly leave the children. Had he forgotten the time when little Flo nearly fell into the well?

Fred's temper was not easily aroused, but this was too much. Pushing aside his plate, he got up and fetched his wife's coat. Bundling her roughly into it, he seized the basket of food.

"Stop tha noise," he said. "I gave thee a present so tha'd enjoy thyself, and I plan to see it used."

4

AT ABOUT the time the train deposited Holly and Fred on the station platform at Skunby-on-Sea, the rector of Tor was beginning his first rehearsal for the 1911 Harvest Concert. The Harvest celebrations, the most important event in Tor's calendar, took place on the last week end in September. In the morning a thanksgiving service was held at the church, after which the congregation marched in procession to the village green, where the Halesowen Silver Prize Band played for half an hour on the gibbet steps. The rector's Harvest Concert, which took place in the afternoon, was presented by the children and the Tor and New Cut Glee

Club, and in the evening, the bell ringers rang one of their longer changes from the church belfry. Almost everybody in the village was involved in the occasion in some way, even the babies—the rector was expected to provide a part for anyone who came, or was brought, regularly to rehearsals. This was not as taxing on Martin's ingenuity as it sounds, for the children's contribution (songs and tableaux) hardly changed at all from year to year, and an extra angel or two could always be absorbed into the back row. Martin would have liked to interest the village in something new from time to time, but innovations, although he insisted on them now and again, were not popular—the audience only really liked to hear their children and grandchildren sing the songs and hymns they had themselves once sung.

On this particular morning, Martin had before him, in the larger of Tor's two schoolrooms, about sixty children, ranging in age from two to fourteen. Among them were four Millers. The fifth had cut the rehearsal and, armed with a threepenny bag of brown sugar, was on her way across the valley to pay a call on a friend.

It was raining, but Gladys kept the sugar dry under her raincoat. As she walked, she sang.

> Nobody told her to go
> From the dear old home,
> Our village is quiet I know,
> She wanted in England to roam,
> The man she married has turned out a scamp
> I'm awfully sorry for Flo,
> But she may return to the home of her birth
> For nobody told her to go.

There were some fifteen verses, each with a chorus, and Gladys had sung them all by the time she came in sight of Hiram Poole.

Hiram Poole was a middle-aged man who lived with his mother, his two brothers, two sisters-in-law and a flock of nephews and nieces in the oldest house in the neighborhood. It is correct to say that Gladys came in sight of him rather than the house he lived in because the Poole home was set into the side of the hill opposite Tor, with a wall that separated it from the road, and Hiram, except in very bad weather, always spent his time sitting on the wall, waving to the passers-by. As soon as he saw Gladys, he removed the battered felt hat he was wearing and waved it excitedly. Gladys held up the bag of sugar and waved back.

Hiram Poole had a very sweet nature and a case of "Derbyshire neck." This disease, a variety of goiter, is believed to be caused by the climate and the water. It is not painful, but it looks ugly. Sometimes the neck swells up until the head looks like a small teacup set in a deep saucer; Lucy Poole, Hiram's mother, had a case of this sort. When Lucy wanted to turn her head, she had to turn her whole body as well.

The Poole home was built in three sections. The oldest part dated from the eleventh century. Pooles had lived there for as long as anybody could remember or any records showed. It was thought that Poole ancestors may have built the original house. Lucy Poole lived in the lower section with Patty, one of her grandchildren. The center section, the oldest one, was occupied by Ezra Poole and his family, and the upper one by John Poole and his wife and children. Hiram occupied a little room at one end of the John family home.

It was the custom among the Pooles for old Lucy to cook for all the others. Two or three times a week, the whole family (including, as often as not, cousins from up the valley) sat down to a huge meal in Lucy's part of the house. On the days when Lucy did not cook, the family lived on left-overs stored in long, narrow cupboards that had been dug out of the hillside behind the John family wing.

None of the Pooles ever kept, or apparently wanted to keep, a job. All of them spent far more of the year out of work than in it. The men did casual farm laboring. Now and again, if she was in desperate straits, Lady Leake would call either on Mrs. Ezra or Mrs. John to help out at Leake Revel, and she would come—if she remembered about it. In the meadow below their little garden, the Pooles kept some scraggy hens and a hutch or two of hare, but these animals bore little resemblance to the excellent game and poultry that were sometimes to be seen roasting in Lucy's oven. It was generally assumed that the Pooles were more successful at poaching than at more lawful occupations.

Actually, Lucy Poole was something of an exception. She did not mind working, so long as it was work around her own home. She strove, in a confused, muddly way, to keep her family fed and clothed, and she did not appear to resent the fact that nobody ever helped her. It was Lucy who found out the dates and times of free church suppers, Lucy who stood in line when clothing was given away, Lucy who knew the hour when jumble sales closed, after which anything that remained could be taken home for free. Since everything the Pooles possessed was either worn out, cracked or broken, life was not easy for Lucy, but she did try. When she was not cooking, she was usually to be found stabbing away at dusty corners with a worn-out broom.

Tor did not look upon the Pooles as desirable society, and some mothers would not allow their children to visit at the house. Holly and Fred, however, encouraged their children to know everyone (anything else would have been bad for trade). They also felt that the Pooles could not be altogether without merit since they shared the Miller fondness for family singing. None of the Pooles had a particularly good voice, but all could sing in tune and hold a part, and they knew an enormous number of folk songs of the kind that tell, in a long succession of verses, some frightful story of murder, rape or desertion. Sometimes, when everybody else in the community was at work, Ezra and John and their wives, and such of their children as had succeeded in playing truant from school, would sit, with perhaps a visiting cousin or two, along the walls of their little paved yard, working their way through the cheerless gloom of some ancient ballad. Hiram would be perched in his usual place, waving to the passers-by, but half turned, facing his relatives, so that he could sing with them. Sometimes several songs would be going on at the same time, but the jangle of sound was never unpleasant. When they were singing together, the Pooles had a kind of strength and warmth and power about them that some of the more solvent but less closely knit families in the village envied. After the Pooles grew tired of singing, all of them but Lucy would simply sit, waiting contentedly and in silence until she had their next meal ready.

The relationship between Hiram and Gladys was one that gave great satisfaction to both of them. Gladys was flattered to have a middle-aged friend, and Hiram thought it marvelous to know a little girl who received regular pocket money. Not that he expected Gladys to spend her money on him—the bags of sugar only reached him very occasionally—but being a man who had never owned money of any kind, he looked upon Gladys' financial status as extremely stylish.

By Poole standards, today was a busy one. Lucy was cooking a meal; Ezra, Hiram whispered to Gladys, had gone into Tor to work, and the rest of the family was in the middle of a song. Gladys climbed up beside Hiram and gave him the sugar. He promptly ripped off one corner of the bag, and tipped it to his mouth as if it were a bottle.

The rain had stopped now, and the dampness of the walls around the Pooles' yard did not prevent the family from sitting outdoors. Among the group, Gladys noticed several Poole cousins, who had apparently sensed Lucy's preoccupation with cooking and had moved in early so as to be included in the meal. Mrs. John conducted the singing. She was a large woman with small pale eyes and hair of such a light blond that it looked white. When she conducted, she waved her arms violently, each upward movement raising the hem of her dress to expose several inches of soiled lace petticoat.

Gladys knew the song well, but she kept her eyes carefully on Mrs. John. The Pooles, for all their general slovenliness, were fussy about their singing, and it would not have done for Gladys to join in unless she was prepared to attend. After a while, Lucy came out into the courtyard, and not long after, Ezra returned home. His morning's work had apparently been profitable. Feeling carefully in the pockets of his sagging jacket, he handed Lucy a large medicine bottle and seven duck eggs.

At the end of the next song, the family adjourned to dinner. Gladys went with them, although no one actually invited her to do so. At the Pooles' house, there was never any question of laying extra places for visitors. Lucy's system was somewhat like the Mad Hatter's: she set as many places as her big table would hold, and then she loaded exactly that number of dinner plates. Nobody was offered a second helping because the family needed the left-overs to live on until Lucy cooked again, but it was expected that all food placed on the table would be consumed, and so anyone who wanted more ate fast, and then moved, or sat next, to a vacant chair. This morning, when all were seated, three extra meals could be seen. Ezra, presumably as a reward for his morning's labors, staked a claim on one of them; Hiram gobbled fast enough to achieve a second, while the third was the subject of a noisy altercation between two of John's boys. During their argument, some of the spare dinner was spilled on the floor, and the boys began to scream and fight. Nobody, however, seemed to notice.

The meal, which was excellently cooked, consisted of jugged hare, potatoes, tripe, cabbage, onions, suet pudding with treacle and generous cups of strong, hot, milkless tea. Even the tea, Gladys thought, has more body to it than the tea I get at home.

Apart from the quarreling boys, the meal proceeded in silence. The Pooles never laughed or joked with each other, and it would have astonished them to know that some people attempt such things while they eat. To the Pooles, a meal was a solemn business, requiring the whole attention, for one never knew how long it might be before one would be served again.

Hiram fell asleep before he had finished his second dinner, so there was nobody to wave Gladys off the premises when she left. She thanked Lucy politely for her hospitality, but Lucy only said: "Next time, dear, stay to dinner with us."

I feel as if I am walking on air, Gladys thought, as she made her way down the hill from the Poole house to the valley road. Any minute now, I might fly. She tried to explain this sensation to the driver of the milk float, who picked her up on his return journey from New Cut, but the cans made so much noise rattling against each other and the float bounced about so badly that Gladys could not make herself heard. The driver dropped her off where he always dropped children off, at the village green. There, talking to a small boy on the gibbet steps (Gladys saw him too late to avoid him) was Martin Hay.

"What happened to you this morning?" The rector sounded annoyed.

Gladys flushed. "I went to see Hiram Poole."

"Didn't you know there was a rehearsal?"

"Yes, but I know all my songs." This was true. Gladys had had the same part in the concert program for several years.

"In that case," the rector said, "let us hear one now."

"In the street?"

"Why not?"

If I didn't find impertinent small girls so infuriating, Martin thought, I should behave better. The child will refuse, and then what shall I do?

But Gladys did not refuse. Walking slowly, and with considerable dignity, up the steps of the gibbet, she turned and sang the rector all the verses of the hymn he disliked most in the world.

Gladys was in no hurry. She suspected that the rector disliked the hymn (it was a favorite in the village and he had tried repeatedly to take it out of the program) and she enjoyed making him listen to it.

"All right, Gladys, thank you. That'll do."

"There's one more verse, Mr. Hay. I'd like to sing that."

If she was mine, I'd spank her, Martin thought, even if she does look so white standing up there. Or does she? Her face isn't white at all—it's green.

Somehow or other, Gladys managed to finish the verse, and then she turned round and was violently sick into the gibbet bird bath.

Martin dashed up the steps. "Gladys! What on earth—"

"It was the Pooles' tea. Oh, oh . . ."

"Tea, hell! There was whisky in it."

5

THE four little Millers who *had* attended the rector's concert rehearsal returned immediately afterward to The Nag's Head, as Mrs. Dutton had told them to do. Edith and Flo, babies of five and three, were made to take naps until dinnertime, Blanche and Lily (Blanche was nine, Lily seven) were allowed to help Mrs. Dutton bake a cake.

"Glad didn't come to the rehearsal," Blanche said self-righteously, as she sifted flour. "She left us when we got to the school."

"She's gone to see Hiram," Lily added.

"Well, that'll be one fewer of you for dinner, then," Mrs. Dutton replied comfortably. "Lucy's cooking today. Rose saw Ezra on the lane first thing, and he told her."

After dinner (cold mutton, potatoes, rice pudding and shandy) Lily and Blanche went down to the long meadow in the valley to watch the whippets run. The idea was Lily's. Usually it was Blanche who decided what the children should do, but today she was in such a good humor that she was willing to let Lily choose. Blanche had just been promoted. This year, for the first time, she was to play the part of the Spirit of Plenty in the Harvest Concert, a job that called not only for flawless Sunday school attendance but also a chubby child. Plenty was the best part in the show—one wore a gold wig and carried a cardboard cornucopia—but up to now, although Blanche held an unblemished Sunday school record, she had lacked the necessary *embonpoint*.

Lily would never be able to play Plenty—she hadn't the build. Already as tall as Blanche and very thin, she was a second edition of Gladys, and she would have given anything to exchange her straight black hair and pale face for pink cheeks and golden corkscrew curls. Lily longed to be beautiful, and, if possible, a princess.

Whippet racing was Tor's, as well as Lily's, favorite sport. With New Cut colliery working around the clock, there were always a certain number of men off duty in the daytime, and most afternoons training excercises were held in the long meadow in the valley. The Tor and New Cut whippets were primarily household pets, and this probably accounted for the fact that they never did very well in intervillage races—they lacked the necessary professional concentration. They were, however, important enough to their owners to be the cause of fights. A whippet was expensive to buy and time-consuming to train, and it mattered a great deal to a man that his dog should stand well with those of his neighbors. The long meadow was a rough, uneven field full of hollows and bumps, on which it was impossible to establish a track that was really fair. The snags in the course were well known to every dog owner, with the result that more time was spent jockeying for places than in any actual racing. Sometimes there would even be no racing at all because the owners of the entries were too busy quarreling, and this meant that if one wanted to see the dogs run, it was best to go to the long meadow on an exercise day, for then they worked all afternoon, if the weather allowed.

When Blanche and Lily reached the meadow, six dogs were exercising, with six more awaiting their turn on the sidelines. Each dog required the services of two men, one at the starting point to hold him, and another at the far end of the field, ready to wave a white handkerchief when he should be released, and to time him with a stop watch. The lean, eager animals, every muscle taut as they flashed across the grass, were thrilling to watch, and Lily usually had eyes for nothing else, but today, only five minutes after they arrived, she lost interest because she noticed a boy on a white pony at the finishing line. Ignoring her sister, she walked over to him.

"It's Jamie Leake," Blanche said as she hurried after. "He's home for a month. Mother pointed him out to me in church."

Blanche was right. For the first time in his life, Jamie was having a holiday at home—and the best time in the world. He looked well, for he was brown from the Swiss sunshine, and he smiled kindly when he saw Lily. He said: "What's your name?"

Lily told him.

"How old are you?"

Lily told him that too.

"You're just a baby. I'm twelve."

"Oh no," Lily said, "Flo's our baby, and she's—"

"My sister just wanted to look at your horse," Blanche explained.

"Did you? You can ride him if you like."

"My sister can't ride, and I don't think—"

"Thank you. I would like to, very much."

So Jamie dismounted, and the groom who was beside him on a quite ordinary brown horse dismounted too, and lifted Lily into the pony's saddle. Off they went, the groom holding the bridle, while Jamie Leake waited beside Blanche.

Now I am really like a princess, Lily thought, riding on a great white horse. She felt less like a princess on the return journey when the groom made the pony trot and she lost the reins and both stirrups, but it was one of those experiences so alarming that she longed for it to go on. Her legs felt so weak when the groom lifted her down that she could hardly stand.

Jamie, who had not spoken to Blanche at all, now politely offered her a ride too. When she refused, he said he thought he should go home now, it was beginning to rain and it looked as if the dogs' exercising would be cut short. Raising his cap to the two little girls, he remounted his pony and rode off after the groom.

The men were leashing the dogs. One of them, who had seen Lily's ride, gave Jamie credit that was not exactly his due. "A right nice lad that, Jamie Leake, doing what he can to see Lily Miller don't fret for her Mum . . ."

The day had been a special one even for the two Miller babies. In the afternoon, they rode around the village on the grocer's dray with young Crew, the grocer's assistant, delivering orders, and then they returned with him to his home, the flour mill (it was said to be a thousand years old and all the machinery was made of wood), for tea. There, in the company of the Crew children, they listened to Mrs. Crew's father, Daniel Park, describe the adventures of two mythical races, the Thumperlumps (a dutiful and dull people) and the Wobbligobs (wicked and amusing). Edith and Flo Miller knew all Daniel's stories by heart. This was just as well, for the mill was a noisy place, and they missed most of what he said.

6

IF THE best kind of vacation is a complete change of scene, Holly and Fred could hardly have chosen better than Skunby-on-Sea. While Tor is high, bleak and shut in most of the year by overhanging clouds, Skunby is flat and open, the surrounding countryside dotted with windmills and striped by dikes and tulip farms. Scenery changes very quickly in England.

Holly and Fred, however, were not interested in scenery. What they wanted most when they arrived at Skunby was a cup of tea. The journey had seemed long, for the train was crowded and traveled slowly, particularly over the last five miles. But here they were at last, with the sun shining brightly down on them; across the end of the station platform hung a big blue banner: SKUNBY-ON-SEA WELCOMES YOU.

"My, Fred, d'you know it's *hot?*" Holly unbuttoned the jacket of her suit—in the end she had worn a suit instead of either of the new dresses she had made. "You know what I'm going to do as soon as I've finished this tea? I'm going for a paddle."

Fred beamed. You wouldn't think to look at her, he thought, that she'd got five fine girls back home. If anything, she's a prettier woman than she was when I married her, and that's talking.

"Stop staring at me, and drink up. We don't want to spend all day in the station."

Fred drank up and paid, adding his pennies to the others in the little pool of tea and milk on the top of the refreshment room counter. Thanking the blonde (who would do nicely for The Nag's

Head if she lived nearer), he picked up the sandwich basket and raincoats and followed his wife into the road that led to the sea.

Already by 1911, selling vacations to the North Midlands had become Skunby's leading industry. The town council, mindful of the natural assets of the place (invigorating air, safe sea bathing, an enormous stretch of level beach and a record of sunshine as high as anywhere in England), aimed to supply amusement for everyone. This was not as difficult as it sounds, for the British expect to enjoy themselves when they are on holiday, and once they have settled in at the seaside, it is not hard to convince them that they are doing so. The fashion for exposing oneself and one's children to a month's sea air every summer, started by the Prince Regent in the late eighteenth century, had by now spread to those families who could only afford a week's annual vacation. At Skunby, from June to September, the whole social life of the place began afresh each Saturday, when the last week's guests went home, and the next week's moved in.

The sea is encroaching along this part of the coast, and so the railway was not brought nearer than a mile from Skunby town. This meant that Holly and Fred had quite a distance to walk from the station to the beach, but since today was Saturday, there was so much to look at that Holly did not find the walk at all long. Most of the neat brick houses that lined Station Road accommodated summer boarders (in the parlor windows were signs that variously read BED AND BREAKFAST, VACANCIES, or POSITIVELY ONLY SMALL DOGS). Mops were being shaken out, doorsteps scrubbed, and long lines of white laundry set to flap dry in the sun. At several front gates, cabs were already drawn up, and fathers and coachmen piled the suitcases and boxes of departing guests on board. Mothers held the hands of sunburned little children, who in turn clutched dolls and spades and buckets and long thick sticks of pink candy. A few very early new arrivals were to be seen (with winter-pale children, wildly excited), and these families quickly bundled their luggage indoors, and bustled off in the direction of the beach, as if they felt they could not afford to miss a minute of their short holiday.

"Dark cottons," Holly complained cheerfully to Fred, "d'you see? Everybody in dark cottons. Not a suit to be seen." She dawdled, staring shamelessly about her, with the result that by the time she reached the sea front her husband was ahead. Fred called: "Shut your eyes. Don't open them till I tell you." Holly giggled. Fred came back, and they crossed the promenade arm in arm.

"Smell the ozone?"

"The what?"

"The fresh air, straight from Denmark. Now look."

Holly opened her eyes. Instead of the open expanse of water that she had expected to see, there was nothing but sand. Far off on the horizon (it appeared to be at least three miles away) a thin blue line showed where the ocean had gone.

"Fred!"

"Don't fret. There's a cart down there we can ride in—see? 'To the Sea—Threepence Return.'"

Sure enough, a deep-sided cart, large enough to hold thirty people, stood facing the ocean, a tired horse between the shafts.

"Ride in a cart nothing! That horse looks overworked to me. We'll walk."

"With all our stuff?"

But Holly was already on the beach, almost out of hearing.

The attractions provided by the Skunby-on-Sea town council were arranged systematically in parallel lines, beginning, and oddly enough ending also, with entertainment for the old folk. Along the promenade were lines of wooden benches, upright chairs, and, every hundred yards or so, a windbreak shelter. These constructions consisted of seats placed back to back with a glass panel between, glass sides and a roof. The seats in the shelters always filled up first, for the wind blows at Skunby all year round. Today, which by Skunby standards was not at all cold, most of the older visitors sat wrapped in overcoats, and the men who wanted to read their newspapers had to fold them in small wads, so that the pages would not blow away.

Along the edge of the beach were the bathing machines—small huts on wheels, each gaily painted, and with a door front and back. These could be rented for threepence the half hour, and while one changed into one's swimsuit within, a horse was attached to the front of the machine, and the whole equipage drawn to the edge of the sea. One entered the water directly from one's machine, and climbed back in again afterward to dress. The horse would then be attached to the shore side of the contraption, and one would make the return journey the same way. This morning, nobody was bathing because the tide was too far out. The machine men sat smoking and chatting near their horses—they would not be doing any business for some while yet.

Holly and Fred found the walk over the sands, past the younger children riding donkeys and the older ones playing cricket, hard going. Ten minutes after they had started, they reached the end of Skunby pier, which stood up out of the sand, dry and tall, its piles coated with barnacles. Holly was waving to a small boy walking along the top when the sea cart with its load of passengers passed them.

Between the end of the pier and the sea, where the sand was firmest, Skunby's most exciting sport was going on—sand sailing. The "boats"—they were light wooden craft pointed at either end and slung between four bicycle wheels—sailed half a mile down the beach and back again. Each boat had a fourteen-foot cutter's sail and a crew of one—it held two passengers. Fred would have liked a ride (the speed was such that some of the time the boats keeled to an angle and rode on only two wheels) but there were several people waiting their turn, and Holly had not yet had her paddle.

With trousers rolled up to the knees, and skirts looped so that only an occasional corner touched the water, the people who had ridden out in the sea cart were already standing in the waves. Very few children were among this group—many appeared to be in their seventies. One old lady had waded out quite far; she stood motionless and alone, staring out to sea. A couple tried to control the behavior of their dog, a shaggy beast with glazed eyes who kept splashing them with his wet, fan-shaped tail. The Millers added their shoes and stockings to the neat row made by the other paddlers. Fred said gently to Holly: "When you're ready, love, take my hand."

The ice-cold water made them gasp. Fred, accustomed to the dull gray light of Tor, screwed up his eyes against the sun. Holly cried: "Isn't this *lovely!* Are you happy, Fred?"

"I'm always happy when you are, you know that."

At two o'clock, the Millers ate dinner at the Elite Café ("For People of Taste—Tripe, Cowheels and Trotters"). The place was large and full of people who, like themselves, had been too busy to eat earlier. Afterward, armed with a bag of candy, Fred and Holly set off up the promenade in the direction of the pier.

As they walked, Fred remarked that he would like to take a nap. Holly agreed. The promenade was crowded now, and it was difficult to make one's way along. Most of the visitors were in family groups, with dogs, and children carrying rubber balls and cricket bats and spades and buckets, spread across the sidewalk. One family, consisting of a father and mother and five little girls, brought a lump to Holly's throat. Fred and I must be the only couple in Skunby without their kids, she thought.

Saturday afternoon was the busiest time of the week for Skunby's street vendors. Tables with little awnings over them were set up at the side of the road; some sellers walked among the people with their wares on trays around their necks. All shouted to attract attention. One man had big balloons for sale, another tiny hats, another celluloid dolls. There were shrimps for sale, and cockles, buns and lemonade, and every size and length of "Skunby rock." This confection, which came in sticks of peppermint pink, had, right through its white middle, SKUNBY-ON-SEA in red lettering. (The charm of this type of candy is that however fast you eat, you never come to the end of the writing until the whole is gone.) Fred bought Holly a hat and some rock and a little dish of shrimps, and he raised his cap to a man with a camera who said an excellent photograph of them both would be ready at a kiosk by the pier in an hour.

As they approached the main shopping street, which went inland from the promenade opposite the pier, Holly and Fred heard cheering and the sound of a drum. Holly ran to see what was happening, and Fred hurried after.

It was the pierrots. Down the street they came, four men in white suits with black pompons for buttons, high white conical hats and broad starched ruffles. Their faces were made up like the faces of clowns—chalk-white, with great red mouths, blue eyebrows and red gashes on their cheeks. The man out front (it was he who was beating the drum) was shorter and older than the others, and every now and again he waved his drumsticks to friends in the crowd, sometimes stopping altogether to speak to a child. When this happened, the two pierrots behind him did splits and handstands, while the crowd applauded. Bringing up the rear, the fourth pierrot

pushed a piano on a handcart. The piano was labeled HULLO, EV-
ERYONE! THE LANSBURY LARKS.

As the pierrots reached the promenade, the crowd stood back to let them pass down a short ramp to the beach. Right below, a little stage had been set up. In front were about thirty rows of deck chairs.

"Fred," Holly said, "I want—"

"I know! Sit at the back then, so I can sleep."

A deck chair at the pierrot show cost no more than a deck chair anywhere else on the beach (twopence) but several times during the performance the actors came among the audience and "bottled," that is to say, presented their collecting bags. The program, which lasted an hour, consisted of songs, guitar playing, short sketches and old jokes. Joe Lansbury had been a pierrot for forty years, and his father had been one before him, with the result that the Larks had an enormous, well-tried repertoire. They advertised "Two different shows every day except Sunday, and a complete change of program twice a week," but actually each program consisted of whatever numbers Joe decided the occasion called for, depending on the weather as well as the day of the week. The Saturday afternoon crowd, for example, when everybody had just arrived in town and was in a generous mood, required a different show from the Friday night audience, which had spent all its money and was due to go back home the next morning. Today, Joe had the people rolling in their seats over a sketch about a pierrot who entered a lady's bathing machine, mistaking it for his own.

The Larks played against a relentless background of wind and waves and shouting candy vendors which would have discouraged all but the most hardened troupers, but this is what the pierrots either were, or rapidly became. They took the programs at such a pace that most of the time the sweat poured down their faces, making puddings of their make-up. Joe did not, however, expect his men to do all the work. He was a great believer in audience participation. During a show, his eyes were everywhere.

"Dad's just dropping off, Mother!" he shouted this afternoon, pointing a stubby finger straight at Holly. "Keep him awake! I need all the men to sing the next chorus."

"Oh, I do like to be beside the seaside. . . ." warbled Fred obediently.

After that it was the ladies' turn. Under a brilliant sun, they accompanied Joe in "Moon, Moon, serenely shining . . ."

Joe's audience was not critical, which was just as well, for there was not really very much talent in his company and the actors had little in the way of clothes, props or scenery to help them. Their costumes were the white pierrot suits they wore, their music came from the ancient piano. When they needed scenery, as, for instance, in the bathing machine sketch, they reverted to the Elizabethan practice of placards, which they pinned to the back cloth curtain that separated the stage from the beach behind. Those pierrots not actually taking part in a number stood back against this curtain and watched their colleagues, laughing uproariously at all the jokes and applauding enthusiastically at the slightest provocation.

What the Larks lacked in talent, however, they made up in vigor. Each man could sing and dance, if tumbling about a stage can be considered dancing, and play the piano and the guitar, and each appeared to possess boundless energy and enthusiasm. One could not help appreciating a pierrot show in which the pierrots made so much effort to please.

The item that Fred and Holly enjoyed most was one in which Joe invited all the children in the audience to come up on the stage and sing with him. The children, as many of them as the little stage would hold, chose a song about a side show at a fun fair, "Come along up in the Flip-Flap."

A little girl (she looked to be about eleven) volunteered to sing the verses. She had a tiny voice, but shrill, and she managed to make herself heard.

"Great, wasn't she?" Fred said afterward as they clapped for her.

"Our Glad could have done as well," Holly replied.

When the show was over, Holly wanted tea. This was available at numerous points along the shore, either in steaming mugs or big metal pots or set out expensively on a tray, with bread-and-butter and cake. The bread-and-butter looked nice, but when one ate it, it tasted gritty. The invigorating breezes of Skunby blew the beach into everything.

After tea, Fred finally got his nap. The Millers rented two chairs in a sheltered corner of the pier, where they were in the sun but out of the wind. Fred fell asleep at once. When he awoke, more than an hour later, the chair beside him was empty.

Holly had no intention of wasting her few precious hours in Skunby napping. As soon as Fred lost consciousness, she returned to the beach. Most of the holiday population of the town appeared to have gathered near the Larks' little stage, and nearly all of them were following Fred's example and sleeping. Holly picked her way among the torpid bodies, puzzled because she saw so few children. In fact, apart from some people swimming—the bathing machine men were busy now—there was almost no activity of any kind. Even the street vendors had gone home.

Then Holly learned from the deck chair man that the children were out walking with Joe Lansbury. Every afternoon, it seemed, Joe organized this walk so as to give the parents a chance to rest. There was no charge for this service (though no doubt the pierrots noticed a difference next time they bottled their way through an audience), for Joe enjoyed the "Lark Walk" as much as anyone. He was proper daft about children, having none of his own, the chair man said.

Holly had no difficulty at all in finding the Walk, for it proceeded about the town quite slowly, singing as it went. First came Joe with his drum, his garish make-up carefully repaired after his activities on the beach, and then, beside and behind him, some fifty or sixty boys and girls. They streamed all over the road and the sidewalks, and such traffic as there was had to make way for them—Joe did not give the road to anyone. Before Holly realized what she was doing, she found herself marching too.

The Lark Walk ended back at the pier. As Joe dispatched the last of his charges, he noticed Holly.

"I got thine here, have I, Ma?" he asked.

"Oh no," Holly was embarrassed. "No, our children aren't in Skunby at all. We—we only came for the day."

"Eh, well," Joe's apple face crumpled into a smile. "Do summat for me, then. Come again next year and bring 'em with you, and stay a week."

"Oh, Mr. Lansbury! Oh, thank you! Yes, I will. . . ."

Which is perhaps why, knowing how Derbyshire women like to keep even the rashest promises (and how difficult it is for any of us to say no to a clown), the Skunby-on-Sea town council placed so high a value on Joe Lansbury's services.

Holly got back to Fred before he had time to worry about her, and she found him sufficiently refreshed by his sleep to be sorry he had missed the Lark Walk. They spent the rest of the evening in the fun fair, getting rid of the remainder of their money: they would have considered it bad luck to return home with any change left.

By the time they boarded the Nottingham train, Holly was very tired. Her face was streaked and dirty, her head ached and her feet hurt. When she remembered, too late, that they had forgotten to call at the pier kiosk for the photograph that had been taken of them, she burst into tears. Fred scolded her gently for doing too much and for not taking a nap when she had the chance to do so; then he settled her head against his shoulder, and sat stiffly upright while she slept.

Looking back on it afterward, Fred decided that the best part of the whole trip was the walk home from Manley to Tor, in the early dawn. The little stone walls between the familiar fields looked as if they had been drawn there with a soft pencil, and the damp air felt friendly and very soothing after all the healthful sunshine he had been subjected to. He had dreaded the day, but it hadn't turned out too badly.

Beside him, Holly wondered how long she ought to wait before breaking it to her husband that next year the trip to Skunby would include all of them, and last a week.

7

SEVERAL weeks after the Millers' trip to Skunby, the rector of Tor dined at Leake Revel, as he did on most Saturday evenings. Dinner was at eight, but Martin was expected to arrive at seven forty-five, in time to join his hostess in a glass of sherry before the appearance, two minutes before the dinner gong sounded, of Lady Leake's daughters and their governess, Miss Cole.

Entertainment at Leake Revel was a curious mixture of the sumptuous and the drab, much like Lady Leake's appearance. Lady Leake had an extensive wardrobe of gowns so ancient and shapeless that they did not seem to belong to her at all, and on these she pinned, haphazardly, jewels of great rarity and worth. Her hair, which was thin and dull and arranged without intent to flatter, was fixed with handsome combs, and on her hands (she cut her fingernails straight across the tops) she wore large, very beautiful rings. In the same manner, excellent wines always accompanied Lady Leake's dinners, but the food was almost invariably flavorless, badly cooked and cold. The cold was not altogether Lady Leake's fault, for the Revel kitchens were situated at the far end of a drafty, cavernous passage, and it had never occurred to anyone in the family either to cover the dishes during their long journey or to supply the dining room sideboard with a warmer.

This evening (it was the last Saturday of September, 1911, and the night before Harvest Thanksgiving), most Tor families were enjoying celebration meals at home, since nobody would have time to cook on the day itself. At Leake Revel, however, no special preparations were made: tonight's dinner consisted of gray, wrinkled mutton, naked-looking boiled potatoes, sodden cabbage and decanted Château Margaux. The conversation turned on the intention of Catherine Leake, aged fourteen, to become a doctor.

"I have told her she must get married first," Lady Leake said. "Women doctors never meet anyone."

"What do you think, Mr. Hay?"

"I think doctors probably meet more people than anybody else, or at least they can, if they want to. What your mother means is that matrimonially eligible Englishmen are apt to be afraid of women with careers."

"Exactly, and a woman without a husband is a great nuisance to her relatives." Lady Leake made this remark without any intention of hurting the feelings of Miss Cole, of whose presence at the dinner table she was hardly aware.

Margaret Leake, the elder daughter, suggested that Martin might provide the solution. If, after she became a doctor, Catherine failed to find anyone to marry her, she could always fall back on him.

"Yes, how about it, Mr. Hay? You would only be my very last resort."

"Well, thank you, my dear, but you know I could never marry into the Leake family. You are all far too grand for me."

Miss Cole giggled.

Catherine said, "I don't think that's fair. Look at that dress Mother has on. It was part of her trousseau."

"Ah! Velvet like this isn't woven nowadays," said her mother.

"I didn't say expensive, Catherine, I said grand." Martin refused tapioca pudding in favor of port-riddled Stilton. "Do you know that some nights I have dinner at home in my dressing gown, and that I don't even bother to shave?"

The girls shrieked.

"What do your callers say?"

"I think they like it. It makes them feel at ease to see me looking comfortable."

"I certainly hope," Lady Leake said, "that if either of you girls inherits Leake Revel, you will not permit your family to dine in this room improperly clad."

"None of us will get the chance, Mother. Jamie adores Revel, and he means to live here forever and ever. He said so."

After dinner, coffee, very pale in tiny Minton cups, was served in the drafty drawing room. When her daughters and Miss Cole had left them, Lady Leake said: "Am I really to let Catherine study medicine?"

"If she wants to, of course, Elizabeth. Sometimes you are very old-fashioned."

"I have the house to consider. Jamie may not live to take over his responsibilities, and in that case Leake Revel will belong to the girls. Of course it isn't very likely that Catherine will need to live here if Margaret does, but all the same—a doctor! We are not a family with brains."

"Perhaps Catherine is the exception. At least she has ambition."

"So it seems. Well, fortunately we haven't got to decide for a while yet, and in the meantime she had better take golf lessons."

They finished the evening with bezique. Just as the rector was leaving, Lady Leake said: "Do you have ambition, Martin, or are you too old?"

Martin grinned. "I used to have flocks of them. Now I think I should die happy if, for one Tor child, I could take the dowdiness out of religion."

"I don't think I've ever heard you preach on that."

"No. The example is all."

"Quite a responsibility."

"Oh, I have my encouraging moments. Didn't you notice tonight? Margaret was quite willing to see me dwindle into a brother-in-law."

8

SEVERAL hours before Martin Hay dined at Leake Revel, the Miller family sat down to their Harvest supper. Crowded into Holly's kitchen at The Nag's Head were Fred and his five daughters, Mrs. Dutton, Rose Dutton, Rose Dutton's young man and the Emney boys, sons of the village plumber, whose mother had been whisked off to Manley Hospital that morning with a burned arm. The table covering the big bathtub was not large enough to seat so many, and smaller, lower tables had been added at either end. The Miller girls wore their best dresses and Fred had on his Sunday suit and his gold watch chain.

The Nag's Head opened for the evening at six, so the inn family always had their Harvest meal at four. During the morning, the Duttons, assisted by all the children, decorated the kitchen with chrysanthemums and sprigs of wheat and gay paper crackers. Holly's dinner consisted of fried ham and roasted hens, potatoes, bread sauce and rhubarb pie with whipped cream. Fred drew pitchers of light ale from the pump in the bar, and there were bowls of black and white humbugs—the largest-sized peppermint candies.

The Miller thanksgiving was a noisy, unhurried affair. Everybody shouted, and helped himself, no one passed anything. The Emney boys, who had been quiet all day, cheered up considerably after receiving their third helpings, and Blanche was urged to keep them company so that she would be sure to look right for the part of Plenty the following afternoon.

"Donald," Fred said to Rose's young man, "how about coming to glee club Monday? We need more tenors."

"Aw, Mr. Miller. I don't rightly think—"

"You go, Donald. Donald sings a treat, Mr. Miller," from Rose.

"Please yourself, of course. It's hard work."

"Practice! Practice!" Gladys teased.

"Anything worth while calls for that, as you'll find out before too many years go by," Fred retorted.

"I've been at my song all week, over and over," Blanche said.

"Well then," her mother's voice was soothing, "you don't need to worry a mite about it any more, do you? You can just sing out, like that little girl your Dad and me heard at Skunby."

"Will she be there next year?"

"I shouldn't wonder."

Holly's remark did not escape Fred; she had not intended that it should. From comments that his wife and children let fall from time to time, Fred already guessed that he would be off on another day trip to Skunby before the next year was out, this time accompanied by the whole family. But he wasn't letting Holly know that he knew—not yet. He wanted the satisfaction of being consulted, and of keeping them all, at least for a while, on tenterhooks. (Afterward, when he pronounced his decision, the children would jump up and down and hug him, and Holly wouldn't say much, just put her arms around his neck, and her lovely mouth on his.)

So now all he said was, "Yes, you be sure and act like you mean it, Blanchie. We don't want a Plenty that looks pinched."

When no one had room for more pie, or another drop of ale, the crackers were pulled, and all put on the paper hats these contained. Then the party adjourned to the bar, where they stood around the piano and sang temperance songs until opening time.

That evening, the innkeeper worked in an orange paper bonnet tied beneath his chin, and Holly and Rose wore fetching tricorns. Once The Nag's Head was open for business, the children had to go back into the kitchen (it is against the law for persons under sixteen to enter a bar), but Gladys, when she thought her mother wasn't looking, opened the door a crack and peeped through. The inn on Saturday nights fascinated her.

What Gladys enjoyed about Saturday nights was not the sight of the barroom itself, which was the same of course as on any day of the week; it was her father's clientele. On Saturdays, a number of New Cut families walked over to Tor to spend the evening drinking with the regular patrons, and these visitors were easily distinguished from the home product both by their physique and by their clothes. The coal miner whose family have been coal miners for several generations, and who has not taken to the work to supplement a farm income the way many Tor men had done, is apt to be short and thickly set, with large muscles. His womenfolk are apt to be short too, and wide in the waist, and all (and this is what interested Gladys) loved bright colors so much that The Nag's Head on a Saturday night resembled a cage of toucans. Although the men's suits were somber, being mostly navy pinstripes, they were garnished either with bright neckerchiefs and brilliant waistcoats or, during the summer, with enormous, home-grown boutonnieres, in which double marigolds predominated. With the navy suits went light brown, highly polished shoes and, as often as not, gaily checked caps. The women liked red, emerald green and bright yellow wools and cottons, and they favored big hats decorated with feathers.

One might have expected that such a cheerful-looking throng would have been full of conversation and laughter, but this was not the case. The Nag's Head bar, even when it was most crowded, was always rather quiet. Those playing the Ring and the Bull, as well as those watching the game, concentrated heavily on the matter in hand, and the people standing along the counter spoke to give an order only when a nod would not suffice. When voices were heard, the sound was melancholy and plaintive, as if the speaker were disappointed both with the quality of his refreshment and the assembled society. The sad note was, however, merely a local accent, the whining tone expressed nothing but contentment and pleasure. Derbyshire mores disapprove of the expression of enthusiasm in public. ("Seein' as tha's gettin' married, Charlie, me and the boys thought tha might accept this set of spoons." "Ah don't mind if ah do.")

Tonight, a subdued group was playing in the alcove, and a silent line, bright as parakeets, stood along the counter. At a table in the middle of the room, three couples shared a platter containing several of Holly's individual meat pies, the women gossiping softly together in voices that threaded in and out of one another like minor-scale arpeggios. On the benches along the east wall, the old men puffed at their pipes, adding their quota of smoke to the blue haze that already enshrouded them. Everywhere was the heady, pleasant smell of good hops.

Presently, someone opened the piano and began to play. At once the customers broke into song, taking up their parts neatly and correctly, like a well-rehearsed choir. The singing continued until long after Holly had caught Gladys peeping through the kitchen door and sent her off to bed. There, warm and snug in the wet cave bedroom, she lay awake listening to the voices below.

Closing time was at ten. After the last guest had gone, Holly went to bed, but Fred stayed downstairs a little longer. Drawing himself a tankard of ale, he made himself comfortable in the alcove under the bull's head. Normally this was his first drink of the day (of course he had a mug or two from the pitcher of beer that stood on the table at meals, but it would not have occurred to anyone in Tor that that was drinking—that was food, and better than milk in Fred's opinion). Today, being Harvest Eve, he had had a pint already, but that did not affect his routine after closing. He did not hurry over this beer, for it was while consuming the soothing liquid that the innkeeper said his prayers. He prayed for the King, the Prime Minister, the Tor and New Cut Glee Club, his daughters, his wife and his job. Then, being English, he prayed for all fishermen and for the Royal Navy, dozing off a little now and then as he did so. Finally he rinsed his tankard and turned out the lights. Holly was already asleep by the time he lay down beside her.

9

Tor's Harvest Sunday began at 5 A.M., when the ringers rang the bells up into the set position and then led them home. The sound woke the sleepers at Leake Revel and the rectory, but most of the village was already up and dressed by that time, and finishing breakfast. Before the bells were quiet, little groups of people began to make their way across the green to decorate the church. They carried sheaves of wheat and barley and baskets filled with fruit, vegetables and shiny pieces of fresh coal.

The decorations were placed quickly, for all had to be finished by the time Martin Hay arrived to take the first service at eight. Like so much else in the village, the scheme used was always the same. Set on a small table halfway up the chancel was the *pièce de résistance*, a model hayrick, eighteen inches high and two feet long, made years before by Daniel Park. (Between Harvests, the rick was kept in Daniel's broom cupboard at the mill, where it had acquired a certain shagginess and a musty smell.) Sheaves of grain were stacked along the nave, fruit and vegetables arranged in the window sills, and the coal was placed at the feet of the lectern and the pulpit. The church at that time of day was very cold, and the stacking, tying and arranging were done with stiff fingers. Even the children were pressed into service—the girls swept behind the workers, the boys carried the rubbish out to the bonfire beyond the churchyard wall.

Tor's Harvest Festival was a fine old custom, but it had one drawback. Almost everybody who took part in it was cross. The domestic celebrations of the night before made early rising unpleasant; husbands were nervous about the morning's band playing, the afternoon's singing or the evening's ringing; and wives were anxious about children who must at all costs be kept clean until nightfall. Martin Hay was harassed by the clock. In spite of the fact that the day's proceedings were repeated every September, he was rarely able to follow a schedule that left him any time for meals.

This year, the celebrations went somewhat more easily than usual, in spite of a too-long anthem from the choir. The reason for this was that, surprisingly, the weather was fine, so there was no delay in the church porch after service while the congregation put on its raincoats and galoshes: the procession from the church to the gibbet led by the Halesowen Silver Prize Band was able to set off immediately. The band always gave its performance in the open air, whatever the weather, and always before a good audience. There were enough musicians of one sort or another in Tor to understand that when a man practices for a specific event, he deserves to have a crowd to hear him, however heavy the rain.

Tor's two-roomed schoolhouse on the green was used for all indoor community activities such as dances, parties and concerts, as well as for weekday and Sunday school. This afternoon, the first members of the Harvest Concert audience to arrive were the Poole family—admission was free. They brought a large contingent of relatives with them, and occupied two full rows of the best seats. Hiram brought his hat, which he waved frequently to his friends just as if he was sitting on the wall back home. Someone had given John and Ezra's children all-day suckers. The room filled up quickly, and the concert began just as soon as the Leake Revel party was seated.

The Sunday school children were responsible for the first half of the show.

Blanche, her chubby knees knocking together, made a decorative Plenty, although her voice was shaky when she had to sing. The babies looked cherubic in their wire and paper halos, and Gladys brought the house down with her rendering of "Rock of Ages"—the hymn she had sung for Martin Hay's edification from the gibbet steps. In this *scena*, which was far and away Tor's favorite, a Poor Soul is discovered clinging to an ivy-covered rock, with an Angel poised above. The Angel, using a tinsel-bound wand which would also make a useful appearance later in the year at Christmas, points the way to Heaven, and sings a hymn about the joys to come; during the last verse, the Poor Soul dislodges herself from the rock, and moves offstage in the direction in which the Angel is pointing. The audience always found this number extremely moving: mothers of members of the cast, Holly included, had been known to weep. Gladys with her long body and black hair was the obvious choice for the Poor Soul; an auburn-haired classmate, with the kind of ringlets Lily pined for, played the Angel.

Gladys always enjoyed "Rock of Ages" very much. This year, at the end of the final verse, instead of following the Angel offstage as she was supposed to do, she collapsed back onto the rock in what was intended to be a demonstration of religious ecstasy, thereby greatly confusing the Angel and covering the stage with a cloud of dust and loose pins. The audience, as she had hoped it might, forgot its company manners and applauded enthusiastically. Only Martin looked put out. He thought Gladys' behavior monstrous, but he was too tired and anxious himself by that time to do more than hurry her off the stage as quickly as he could, thankful that his part of the Harvest Concert was over for one more year.

The second part of the afternoon was the responsibility of the Tor and New Cut Glee Club. Gladys sat in the wings for this, watching her father. Fred sweated with stage fright. He loved to sing, but he had a poor memory and not much ear, and his pride and pleasure in belonging to the glee club was marred by the torture that it was to him to sing in concerts. During "Ave Maria" he completely lost his way and, while trying frantically to get back on beat, he was shocked to see his eldest daughter wink at him.

"Proper irreverent, you were," he said to Gladys afterward. "Suppose anybody but me 'ad seen you? I'll 'ave you remember that people don't sing serious to be laughed at."

"Oh, really, Dad! I can't see why they shouldn't."

10

It was cold: the damp, penetrating cold in which Tor excels in the wintertime. Even indoors, beside a fire, it was difficult to keep warm, and where Gladys Miller stood, on top of an upturned soapbox outside the northeast corner of the school building, the wind seemed to whistle straight through her body. The snow had fallen early; it was only mid-November, and yet already a deep layer covered the moors and hills. Gladys could not feel her fingers; even blowing on her woolen gloves made no difference. She would have liked to stamp her feet, but the soapbox wasn't up to it, and she could not leave her post. Being the tallest member of Martin Hay's Sunday school, her job was to watch through the window and warn the other children when the rector left the inner classroom, where he always stayed after school was over to check the registers left for him by the other teachers. Outside the main door, keeping a watchful eye on Gladys, the rest of the Sunday school waited, armed with snowballs.

Every winter, on the first Sunday when there was thick snow, the children played this game with the rector. Martin was not supposed to know about it in advance, but he made his preparations too, as well as the children—putting on his heaviest pair of overshoes, and spending rather longer than usual examining the registers, so as to give the children time to get themselves organized. Once he had received the shower of snowballs that would greet him at the door, his job was to run after the children and catch them if he could. He never did catch them, though for a lame man he really ran very well.

This afternoon, from her perch on the soapbox, Gladys had a fine view of the village; across the valley, she could just see the rooftops of Lucy Poole's house. With so little new building in the neighborhood, the appearance of Tor did not change much over the generations; a barn might be repainted, a wall dividing two fields pulled down, a sheep shelter moved from one part of a meadow to another—little else. Among the oldest landmarks were some hummocks far up the ridge which were all that remained of a Roman soldiers' camp. ("You've heard of Julius Caesar? Come, come. You must have heard of him." "Yes, of course, Mr. Hay. Only I thought his name was Julius Cariot.") Far below, to the south, beyond the cottages and The Nag's Head, the largest of the neighborhood swimming holes was just visible, its surface white with snow-covered ice. Against the horizon, the chimneys of New Cut colliery stood clearly outlined. The children at the schoolhouse door whispered and giggled. From somewhere a long distance off a donkey brayed.

One of these days, Gladys thought, as she looked away from the window at the familiar countryside, one of those little cottages will belong to me. My husband and I will have a garden, and at least six sons, and evenings, when he's washed the coal off and had his tea, we'll sing duets together. Maybe Mother will come over and play our accompaniments. . . .

Suddenly she realized that Martin had already passed her look-in window and was almost at the door. Shouting the warning, Gladys sprang off the box and ran as fast as she could down the rough path that led to the lane. She had farther to go than the others, but she ran faster, and she was out of sight of the school before she slowed down enough so that the first of the other children caught up with her.

With his biretta jammed down over his ears and his cassock looped over one arm, Martin dodged the barrage of snowballs as best he could and thundered down the hill after the children, the fiercest expression he could muster fixed to his face and his black petticoats flapping ominously as he ran.

Gladys had given so short a warning that the older children in the group forgot all about taking care of the younger. Usually they were careful to see that nobody was left behind, but this time several members of the babies' class had to scatter into the snowdrifts at the sides of the path to avoid Martin as he pounded by. Only one continued down the hill. In her efforts to catch up with her sisters, Flo Miller split first one seam and then the other of her rompers. Finally, as was only to be expected, she fell. The rector could not stop. Gathering his garments against himself, he leaped clean over the shrieking child.

Some hours later, after Flo's self-confidence had been restored with cookies and her damaged pride smoothed over with a large slice of fresh Bakewell tart (fortunately, no physical damage had been done), Holly said severely to her four older daughters: "I've told Baby she need never go to Sunday school again as long as she lives, so it will be all the fault of you girls if she grows up atheist."

"Oh, Mother. How could we know Gladys wasn't going to give us proper warning? She was daydreaming."

"Daydreaming or not, it's the place of all of you to look out for each other. I know Mr. Hay only meant it for the best—and since there wasn't a one of you to be seen, I don't know what else he could have done—but it only made Flo worse to be carried home. I thought she was dead, poor little mite, the way she was screaming."

When they were alone, Fred said to his wife: "You don't really expect the girls to mind each other all the time? Seems to me they shouldn't have to do that."

"Fred Miller, that's just what I *do* mean. The strength of this family lies in us all sticking together, and our girls can't learn that too soon for my money."

11

CHRISTMAS came and went, with its parties, carol singing, candy-filled stockings, turkey, plum pudding, holly and mistletoe, followed by two months when almost everybody in Tor had a cold in the head, and Fred's biggest sales were in hot, mulled wine. And then, with February scarcely gone, spring came, with primroses in the meadows and the hawthorn in bud.

The first social event of the year in Tor was the annual pet show, held in April. This was an important occasion for Fred, for not only did he do a great deal of business during the two days of the show (he served more customers then than at any other time of the year), but he always entered several of his rabbits. So far, in spite of years of effort, he had never managed to win a prize, although he usually came away with something: the carriage-house doors at The

Nag's Head were covered on the inside with honorable mentions. This year, however, when all the rabbit entries were arranged in their boxes around the inn yard (fortunately it always seemed to keep fine for the two days of the show) it was clear to everyone that Alice, Fred's large gray doe, outshone every other creature. So Fred went about his heavy day's work singing gaily, and Holly did the same. Once she had seen Alice's competitors, she guessed that this evening would be just the time to tell Fred about the week at Skunby.

The children kept busy all day too, for they always entered all the animals they had. This year, Lily owned a black kitten and Gladys two white rats. All the Miller children owned rabbits. The judges were highly knowledgeable whippet owners from Manley, but they judged the children's mongrel entries just as seriously as their parents' pedigreed ones. The little Millers, like their father, were not in the habit of winning prizes, so it was an exciting moment for all of them when Alice received her gold ribbon. Fred was so overcome with emotion that he called for a round of beer on the house, even though the place was so crowded one could barely make one's way through to the bar counter.

During the pet show, the bar stayed open an hour later than usual, so it was midnight on the evening of Alice's triumph by the time Fred came upstairs to bed. He found Holly awake, naked, sitting up against the pillows. (Holly would have thought it vulgar for a married woman to wear clothes in bed.) She broke it to him at once that she had reserved rooms for them all in a boardinghouse at Skunby called The Dunes, for the whole of the first week of August.

Fred was speechless. "These Dunes," he said at last, "what is it?"

"A lovely place—owned by Mrs. Dutton's cousin! Wasn't it a coincidence? I just happened to mention that we'd thought of going to Skunby and didn't know where to stay, and she said—"

"*We* thought! *We!* What if I say no?"

Holly changed her tone. "We can afford it," she said in a small, injured voice. "I know as well as you do business has been good."

Whatever I say, she'll trap me, Fred thought.

"A day is one thing," he grumbled. "But a week! A whole week!"

"You need a holiday, love."

"I done passably without one all these years. No! If you want to go to Skunby, you go, and take the kids with you. But I'm not moving."

"Oh Fred—" Holly's eyes were brimming—"you wouldn't make me go all that way alone, would you? It wouldn't be fair."

"Art fair to me, talking of all this uprootin', and looking the way tha is?"

12

HOLLY had needed a month in which to prepare for one day at Skunby-on-Sea, and so, when she intended to spend a week there, Fred thought it likely that The Nag's Head would be in a state of turmoil all summer. It surprised him, therefore, when his wife's sewing and packing took only a few hours—he did not realize that she had been planning for the trip all year. She had also been doing some planning for him. She had approached the Duttons and Fred's closest friends in the glee club, and they, as before, promised to take care of the inn while the Millers were gone. Fred's own arrangements were, therefore, very easily completed. From Fred's point of view, this was unfortunate. He felt, rightly, that he had been inveigled into this holiday and he would have welcomed a chance to complain about it. But even the appalling business of loading his family into the train on time was achieved with smoothness, in spite of all the luggage Holly felt she must take.

As often happens in a situation of this sort, Fred's disinclination to enjoy himself was short-lived. Skunby-on-Sea turned out to be different from the way he remembered it. This year, the place seemed full of pleasant, companionable people and interesting things to do. Fred's discovery would have delighted the Skunby town council had they known of it, for the Millers were exactly the kind of family they were most anxious to please. All that had been required to effect Fred's change of heart was an inn equipped with comfortable armchairs and his own brand of beer, a few other silent, male visitors, and a first-class, beautifully cared-for bowling green.

The game of bowls is played with black wooden balls which are rolled over a smooth lawn, and the object is to make them come to rest as close as possible to a white jack. The balls all have a bias, that is, they are weighted off center, and will not roll in a straight line to a stop. The skill lies in the rolling—a fast ball curves less than a slow one. Fred had often watched the game, but he had never played it. Now, with three men who also liked his kind of beer, he began to learn. He found that he enjoyed bowling so much that, except when dragged away once or twice by his family, he spent the rest of his holiday at the green.

Holly, of course, had the children to look after, but she did not let this fact prevent her from indulging in *her* favorite occupations: gossiping (with Mrs. Pegler, the landlady), staring at the people and buying candy and trinkets from the peddlers on the sea front. She also paid her first visit to a professional hairdresser—a frightening experience that she considered well worth it. She returned very pleased with herself and looking like a startled Dutch doll, her round face framed in hard, tight, sausage-shaped curls.

As for the little girls, who can say what Skunby meant to them? The place was Paradise. They built sand castles, rode donkeys, paddled and swam; they caught their toes in the claws of crabs and stung themselves on jellyfish. The sea and the sunshine burned their faces until their scorched skins flaked and peeled. Edith one day wedged her head inside her sand bucket and had to be extricated by the doctor. All of them ate enormously of Mrs. Pegler's large, starchy meals: breakfast at eight, dinner at one, high tea at five, cookies and cocoa at nine, and nothing off the bill if one ate out.

It was a vigorous life, and nobody entered into it with more spirit than the Peglers. During the summer months, that family slept on cots in the greenhouse so that guests could be squeezed into every available corner of their home. Discipline was strict. A notice under the hat rack in the hall said:

WELCOME!
Children must be kept Under Control.
Guests who are late for meals will not be served.
COME AGAIN!
V. Pegler

Like the rest of the boardinghouses in Skunby, The Dunes did not expect to see its guests during the day except at mealtimes. This custom assured the Lansbury Larks of their morning audiences—

holiday-makers turned out into the street at 9 A.M. are mostly willing, by eleven, to pay twopence for the rent of a chair.

This summer, the Larks were a little grander than they had been the year before: they now had the use of an indoor theater. The new arrangement meant that the company was able to play in the evenings, and also in any weather, though Joe still kept the beach platform and gave his two daytime shows outdoors if he could. At the evening performances, which lasted two hours and cost sixpence, one had a tip-up seat, no "bottling," and for a penny extra a printed program.

Joe's indoor theater was at the end of the pier, out over the water except at low tide. The Skunby town council had roofed in a section of the structure and added a stage, a couple of dressing rooms and seating accommodation. The dressing rooms enabled Joe to bring two women into the company, his wife Mae, who sang, and a young girl, Bettine Rowe, who danced. Mae Lansbury was a large-bosomed lady with a roof-shaking contralto, immediately popular with the Skunby audiences. Bettine was popular too. After the intermission, when the company changed from their pierrot costumes into evening dress, Bettine danced in a sleeveless blouse and a long skirt that was slit up the sides to expose her slender legs.

Holly had, of course, told the children about the Lansbury Larks —she and Fred had sung "I Do Like to Be Beside the Seaside," and some of the other songs. She had also described the pierrots' clothes, the white suits with black pompons, and the high white conical hats. Even Martin Hay had talked of them, describing how the pierrots dated back beyond Shakespeare's time to the traveling theatrical companies of medieval Italy. The result of this was that Gladys, always bored by the rector's discursions into history, thought of the pierrots as something old-fashioned and foreign. When Holly suggested, on their first evening in Skunby, that they all pay a visit to the theater on the pier, she agreed, but she was not particularly enthusiastic.

Maturity, if a woman reaches it at all, is arrived at either in small, unconscious steps, or violently, jolt by jolt. Gladys was one of the jolters. Until this moment, her knowledge of the stage was limited to Martin Hay's productions in the village school and to concerts presented by the Tor and New Cut Glee Club. The Lansbury Larks' show, which was much the same as hundreds of other pierrot shows going on in makeshift theaters around the British coast (it was, in fact, of a lower standard than many) introduced her to a world of glamour and delight which for the rest of her life never ceased to enchant her. Although the Larks' white suits were patched, dusty, and creased (it was getting toward the end of the season) and the actors more than once fluffed their lines, Gladys found nothing that was short of perfection. Throughout the performance, she sat tense on the edge of her chair, with a disturbance going on inside her as if she had just swallowed a live eel.

The evening began quietly enough. The pier theater was bare, drafty and uncomfortable; it smelled of seaweed and disinfectant. The tide was high. Between the widely spaced floorboards under their feet, the audience could see water swirling greenly about. Fred squeezed an empty matchbox through, and the children watched it rise and fall on the slow waves before it moved sedately out of sight. The place was brightly lighted with yellow electric bulbs whose glare was reflected harshly by the whitewashed walls. The seats, which were hard and small and arranged too close together, squeaked when they were sat upon. Pink cotton curtains draped the back of the wide, shallow stage, and against them, in a semicircle, were set five white wooden milking stools. Downstage to the left stood a white-painted upright piano.

Fifteen minutes before the performance was due to begin, all the seats had been sold to an audience which ranged in age from eighty to six weeks. Most were in family groups, whose members munched steadily on apples, oranges, nuts and candy, drawn at frequent intervals from rustling paper bags. The Millers arrived early, well supplied by Fred with sticks of Skunby rock and peanuts. Lily would have liked to do things stylishly and have a program, but she had no money and Fred thought the additional purchase an extravagance.

The show began punctually at six-thirty, with the arrival on the stage of John Cook, Joe Lansbury's pianist. Cookie, as the company called him, wore the usual pierrot costume with its wide starched ruffle but, instead of a tall hat, he had on a small black skull cap, the headgear that the Larks had adopted this year because four of their six tall hats had worn out. (The caps are an alternative part of the pierrots' traditional costume.)

Cookie was a small man of slight build, with a middle-aged appearance, although on this, the first occasion Gladys saw him, he was not more than twenty-five. He had been in the entertainment business since he was eight years old and, while pierrot shows lasted, it was unlikely he would ever be out of a job. He could play the piano and the guitar and the drums, as well as sing, dance and act a little.

Now, with a hard white spotlight picking him up, Cookie played a medley of songs. He played softly, without looking at the keys, talking to the audience as he did so.

"Mrs. Bell! How are you, Mrs. Bell? My, you got the twins with you tonight—ain't that fine? That was Mrs. Bell from last summer, folks. My friend, Mrs. Bell."

Presently he changed key and played "Here We Are Again."

> Slap, bang, here we are again,
> Here we are again, here we are again,
> Slap, bang, here we are again,
> And a jolly lot are we. . . .

"Come along, now. Have you all forgotten how to smile?"

The audience warmed to this coaxing, and by the time Cookie finished and the house lights had gone out with a click, they were more than ready to greet the rest of the Larks as they came tumbling through the pink curtains. Lining up in front of the footlights, the company sang:

> Kiss the girl if you're going to,
> And let her go home to bed.
> All night long you've been heard,
> Pecking at her just like a bird,
> Give the girl a nice long loud one, Fred!
> One of the sort she can't rub off
> And let her go home to bed.

This song, of course, convulsed the Millers, and Joe, who guessed the reason and never let an opportunity pass him by, pointed at Fred and said: "Do stop eating nuts, Fred! It's a big 'ole tha's got there. Tha'll never fill it."

Joe, Mae Lansbury and Bettine then withdrew to their white stools, while the two young pierrots, Eddie and Max (a different

pair from last year), held a repetitive little conversation on the subject of gardening:
"I hear you've got a very fine garden, old boy."
"Oh, yes. I certainly *do* have a fine garden."
"What do you grow in it, old boy?"
"What do I grow in it?"
"Yes, what do you grow in it, old boy?"
"Well, I grow scoxias, obnoxias, meershams, blue and white nutmegs, antigodandicums . . ."
"Antigodandicums! What in Heaven's name are antigodandicums?"
"You mean to tell me you've never heard of antigodandicums?"
"That's right. I ain't never heard nothing about antigodandicums."
"Why, *everybody's* heard about antigodandicums! They're a cross between a cowslip and a cabbage, they flower like a hollyhock, and fruit like a cucumber. But it's the smell that really counts."
"The smell?"
"Yes, the smell."
"What's it like?"
"What's the *smell* like?"
"Yes, old boy, what's the smell like?"
"Well, it's a kind of mixture of chutney-bush and potato-chip plant, and Skunby railway station the first day one gets down here for a holiday. . . ."

The next item was a dance from Bettine. Bettine and Mae Lansbury were in pierrette costume—black caps, white jackets that buttoned with black pompons, and short, stiffly starched white skirts that flared sharply from the waist. With these they wore long black stockings (both ladies possessed well-shaped legs) and high-heeled white shoes with black pompons for buckles.

Bettine's dance was followed by guitar playing by Cookie, Eddie and Max. Meanwhile, Joe kept busy in the background trying to repair his milking stool. Each time he sat on it, something gave way, throwing him to the floor. First one leg would go, and then another, and Joe would work patiently away, using enormous, highly colored tools that he did not really have any idea how to manipulate. Now and again he would stop his work and bustle forward to tell the audience a story ("The doctor says to the young lady, 'What you need, my dear, is a little sun and air.' 'Oh doctor,' she says, 'oh doctor, but I'm not married.'") Then back he would go to his stool, beaming with pleasure, only to have it collapse under him again the moment he sat down.

Each item in the program followed quickly on the last just as it did in the Larks' program outdoors. Joe was never still a second except when his wife was singing. Mae had a large repertoire of throaty love songs, with rippling piano accompaniments that called for, and got, a complete and admiring silence while she sang, and prolonged applause when she stopped.

At the end of the first hour there was an intermission during which cups of tea, lemonade and ices were sold; Larks' audiences had an unlimited capacity for light refreshment. At the end of the second half, which was much the same as the first except that the pierrots wore evening dress, Joe and Mae sang their most popular number:

> We've been together now for forty years,
> An' it don't seem a day too much.
> There ain't a lady livin' in the land
> As I'd swop for my dear old Dutch. . . .

Afterward, the Larks jumped down from the stage to shake hands with their friends and sign autographs, and when finally the audience began streaming home down the dark pier, they felt, as Joe had intended them to feel, as if they had spent the evening among friends at a party, rather than watching a stage performance.

Gladys did not speak until the Millers reached The Dunes. Then she said to her mother, "I don't believe I shall ever be quite the same again—never, never."

Holly replied sympathetically, "Of course you will, dear. It was the heat. Take a stomach pill before you go to bed. I brought some with me."

13

EACH day of the Millers' holiday began in the same way, with an argument about Holly's time: everyone had a different use for it.

Fred wanted his wife to bowl with him; Edith and Flo needed her to build sand castles and paddle; Lily wanted to be taken to the terrace of the Grand Hotel for tea and ices; Gladys could not see what else her mother had to do but attend performances of the Lansbury Larks. Blanche's demands involved the whole family—she wanted them all to accompany her to the twice-daily services of the Young Christian Army.

Holly did her best to oblige everybody by shredding her day into the required number of pieces. She enjoyed everything her family planned for her except the Young Christians. This tiresome brigade, led by a curly-haired curate with an expansive, cavalier manner, descended to the beach the first thing every morning, and with an energy that could, Holly felt, have been better directed elsewhere, dug pews in the sand and set up a harmonium, a reading desk and a quantity of brightly colored pennants. Blanche Miller worshiped the curate on sight. When his confident, vacuous smile was flashed in her direction, she blushed to the roots of her hair and went about her spading with renewed vigor. She hurried from the Dunes immediately after breakfast each day so as to be among the first to break ground at whatever site the Reverend Fox decided was safe from the incoming tide. The curate no longer consulted the local boatmen on this subject. More than once, after he had taken their advice, his flock of earnest little boys and girls had had to interrupt their devotions and jump for it out of crumbling pews.

The Young Christians promoted Blanche from private to corporal and from corporal to sergeant, replacing her green armband with a red-and-gold one. Blanche's devotion to God and man being about equally divided (though with something of a list in favor of the Reverend Fox), she found her family's disinclination for religious observance encouraging—no missionary worth his salt ever had things easy. Actually Blanche's efforts to coax the Millers into the damp, sandy seats she worked so hard to prepare met with occasional success, for the Young Christians were difficult people to avoid. If one did not attend their gatherings, one was plunged after by children waving collecting boxes and holy pictures, whereas the services themselves were always short and pleasantly rowdy, with hymns extraordinarily like the choruses of the Lansbury Larks:

Oh for a man—
Oh for a man—
Oh for a mansion in the skies!

The fifth day of the Millers' holiday was Lily Miller's birthday. Mrs. Pegler allowed Lily to choose the dinner menu—roast pork with crackling and applesauce, baked potatoes, hot chocolate pudding—and in the afternoon the whole family had tea and ices on the terrace of the Grand Hotel. The meal there was expensive and inadequate; one ate tiny cakes with a two-pronged fork, and the teapot was delivered to the table without a cozy, but the charm of the place for Lily was that one could watch the *haut monde* of the North Midlands go by. ("Earrings! Just look at them earrings, Mum. When'll I be old enough to 'ang some on?")

As a gesture to her sister's birthday, Gladys missed Joe Lansbury's afternoon show, but otherwise she attended every performance the Larks gave that week. In the mornings and afternoons she went by herself, thereby mortgaging her pocket money well into the autumn, and in the evenings, Holly and Fred took her.

By now, Joe Lansbury was aware of Gladys' attachment to the pierrots. Indeed, he could hardly have failed to be, for Gladys always sat in the front row and never missed a chance to come up on the stage and sing with him when he asked for volunteers.

"My!" he would shout. "Here comes that long drink of water again. Tell 'em where tha's from, lassie."

"Tor, Derbyshire."

A ripple of laughter would go through the audience at this. Tor's weather was well known.

"Thirstiest place in the nation," Joe would say. "Got to be a long drink of water, living there."

It disappointed Holly that Joe did not invite any children to sing alone this year. Instead, he pretended to bake a cake for them on the stage, using a candle, a big covered tin and a song, made up of nonsense words. The finished cake was then divided and eaten—a poor substitute, Holly thought, for a solo from her Gladys.

And so, all too speedily, the Millers' week at Skunby came to an end. Mrs. Pegler kissed Holly and the children good-by, assuring them over and over that their rooms would be ready waiting for them at the same time next year. Fred and his friends at the bowling green exchanged addresses. All winter long they would send each other post cards, commenting on the weather and ending "Hoping this finds you as it leaves me, Respectfully. . . ." Fred was astonished to find that it was quite a wrench for him to leave Skunby, though he was very pleased indeed to see The Nag's Head again, and find everything safe and in good order. Holly, as soon as she had unpacked, made the little girls a set of pierrot costumes out of some old sheets, and Gladys taught her sisters to sing as many of Joe Lansbury's songs as she could remember. When she had them as word-perfect as she was herself, she wrote and told Joe. He did not reply, although she wrote several times.

14

IN THE lives of all of us, the events that mark what prove later to have been major turning points are often accidents, or happenings so insignificant that we hardly notice them at the time. Because of a cold in the head, we do not go to the party and we are home when the telephone rings; or because we forget our key and have to go back for it, we catch a different taxi from the one that was slowing down for us when we first signaled; and because of one of these small incidents, our lives are irrevocably changed. Tor's Harvest Concert that autumn—1912—was just such a turning point for Gladys Miller. There was nothing particularly outstanding about the program or the cast, for both were much the same as on other occasions. What was different was that the audience contained, altogether against his will, an elderly Welshman named Lloyd Morgan. Mr. Morgan had come to Tor to judge an area glee club competition that was being held in New Cut the following afternoon, and the only suitable train from Wales set him down in the Tor valley sixteen hours before he needed to be there. As the house guest of the rector, Mr. Morgan had not had the courage to refuse to attend the village concert, so there he was, bored and resigned, in the middle of the front row.

Gladys knew about Mr. Morgan and she decided to see if she could impress him with her singing. This year, Martin had given her "O for the Wings of a Dove," a piece that the soul of every glee club judge in England aches from hearing, and so when Gladys began, Mr. Morgan's ears were as deaf to her as he knew how to make them. But she sang so well that when she finished, he rose to his feet. It was a new experience to have a little schoolgirl make that worn aria sound so fresh.

After the concert was over, Mr. Morgan hunted up Holly and Fred and told them, categorically and without a doubt, that Gladys had the makings of a great singer: her voice must be professionally trained.

And this is where the accidental turning point comes in.

If Mr. Morgan had not chanced to be at the Harvest Concert, or if Holly and Fred had been able, as they were not, to discount his praises as the biased opinion of a satisfied Nag's Head customer, Gladys might really have distinguished herself as a serious singer. The old gentleman had been right in what he said about the potentialities of her voice. As it was, thanks to a variety of influences, not the least of which was the teacher Holly and Fred picked for her, Gladys made a name for herself, but in a very different world. She became famous as an entertainer and comedienne in the movies, though not until she was a middle-aged woman. That, however, is another story.

Mr. Morgan's remarks were, of course, all over Tor in no time. The Nag's Head clientele spoke of nothing else, much to the innkeeper's delight and embarrassment. Fred and Holly were bewildered. They were as eager as any parents are to do the best for their children, but the whole business posed a number of problems about which Holly was less happy than Fred. To Holly, Gladys' sudden leap to local fame cast a menacing shadow—the shadow of five little girls growing up and leaving home, and thus breaking up the unity of the family.

Manley, Tor's nearest town, was purely an industrial center that in 1912 had no singing teachers, but twelve miles north of the village, in Chesterfield, there was Madame Lola's School of Voice. The Millers knew about Madame Lola because several of the daughters of the wealthier farmers in the neighborhood went to her for lessons—it was fashionable at the time for young women to have their voices trained. Madame Lola was, however, a luxury beyond the reach of The Nag's Head Inn at the best of times, and far beyond it now, when the Millers had so recently enjoyed a week's vacation at Skunby-on-Sea. Holly and Fred did not know what to do, though they were in no doubt at all that, somehow or other, Gladys must have her lessons. Transportation, at least, was no problem. A bus ran from Tor to Chesterfield every Saturday morning, returning to the village in the early afternoon. Fred prayed about his daughter as he sat with his pint under the bull's head after closing time, while Holly, in the bedroom upstairs, took her courage in both hands and wrote to Madame Lola, asking how soon Gladys could start.

Both appeals received prompt replies. Madame Lola wrote by return, on pink, scented notepaper, to say that she would be delighted to see Gladys on the first Saturday after Christmas, and the New Cut Miners' Welfare Organization came forward with an offer to pay all Gladys' musical expenses for six months.

The New Cut Miners' Welfare was a charitable institution founded by the miners themselves, and paid for by small compulsory dues. It operated a community building in New Cut equipped with a bar and billiard rooms, and it nearly always had more money in the kitty than it knew what to do with. Too much cash in hand was not considered wise, and Gladys Miller presented the committee with an excellent excuse both for spending money and for obtaining first-class publicity. It never occurred to anybody that Gladys was not a coal miner's daughter and did not even live in New Cut— The Nag's Head was sufficiently a part of that community for the men to think of her as one of themselves. When the news was made known, Holly wept, and Fred became misty-eyed, and the Manley *Reporter* published a story about it on the front page, with a snapshot of Gladys, and a studio portrait of the president of the Welfare.

"And what does young Gladys have to say to all this?" Lady Leake asked the rector. "I spoke to Holly and congratulated her. I haven't seen the child."

"Oh, she's very much excited, but that's only to be expected."

"She won't get anywhere, of course. They never do. In a village like this where we have no child who *can't* sing, we are bound to produce a better-than-average voice now and again. I remember James taking a great deal of trouble over a young Pepperday, who we all thought sang brilliantly."

"What happened to him?"

"He went off to have his voice trained, and the results were appalling. Perhaps if James had paid for him to go to London, things would have been different, but Tor people never want their children to leave home, so the boy studied locally. In Bolsover, I believe."

"I shall be sorry if that happens to Gladys."

"It will." Lady Leake glanced at Martin. "You must have found Mr. Morgan convincing!"

"Well, I had him in the house overnight."

"Gladys Miller's an extraordinarily plain child."

"Yes, indeed. Though that's part of her charm."

15

CHRISTMAS meals and Christmas music (Gladys sang "O for the Wings of a Dove" again, once in church and several times in the bar of The Nag's Head) are no way to calm a child's nerves. The night before Gladys was due to go to Chesterfield for her first lesson with Madame Lola, she hardly slept, and when she did it was to dream that the Lansbury Larks were performing on the gibbet steps, with herself in Joe Lansbury's role.

At six in the morning, when the colliery whistle blew, Gladys got up. It was still dark but, by the light of the street lamp outside the window at the end of the second floor corridor, she watched the Tor men who were on the early shift begin their walk to New Cut. They passed the inn in little groups, two and three together, their dark work clothes as alike as uniforms, and their peaked cloth caps set back to front on their heads. None spoke. Each man carried a dinner pail, and, separately, a bottle of cold tea. All wore wooden-soled shoes that clacked on the cobbles. In the lamplight, the men's faces looked alike too—round, white buns that were puffy from insufficient sleep.

Holly had heard the children's door open, and guessed where she might find her daughter. Gladys was crying.

"Mum, I can't take their money. I can't."

"They want you to, dear."

"Suppose I don't turn out good?"

"They didn't give it to you to turn out good."

"I'm cold. . . ."

Holly unbuttoned her dressing gown and wrapped it cozily around the two of them.

"When the men gave you that money," she said gently, "they did it partly so you could have fun, but mostly I expect it was because somebody a long time ago gave *them* money when they needed it. You're their chance to say thank you. That's the way life is, or anyway it's the way it seems to be in Tor. You'll get your chance to thank them one day, even if you can't now." Suddenly Holly's voice changed and became severe: "There goes young Micklem and Rabie Andrews. They had a couple more than they should've last night. I knew they'd be late for work."

Gladys said: "Mum, you don't understand. It isn't that I can't say thank you—I've been doing nothing else for weeks. It's just that —suppose I fail?"

"Love, you can't fail. You may not turn out a singer, but who'll fash themselves about that? All we want is for you to be yourself."

"I wish I knew what that was."

Holly hugged her. "A big risk, if you ask me. But your Dad and me took it, and so can the Welfare. And you."

Their giggles woke Fred. He had not been sleeping too well lately either.

"What's all the noise about?" he called.

"An early breakfast for once," Holly answered promptly, "and kippers for everyone who's down in ten minutes."

Part II

1

MADAME LOLA was a large woman of fifty, with peroxide blond hair, frequent headaches and a tightly corseted figure. Since she had a very small head, she always gave the impression that she was a little farther away from one than she really was. She had an extraordinary talent. Without either musical ability or teaching skill, she ran an extremely profitable establishment for improving young women's music and manners. Most of her students were in their late teens or early twenties, and it was their ambition to sing, to move well and to eradicate the whine in their speech. Madame's expensive treatment did not enable them to achieve completely any of these aims, but her system was such that nobody ever entered the Chesterfield School of Voice without emerging, like Bottom, at least partially translated.

The Chesterfield School of Voice occupied the ground floor of Madame Lola's home, a brick house at the intersection of two busy downtown streets. Buses passed close to the door. Madame Lola's rooms upstairs were shaded, perfumed and crowded with bamboo furniture and little potted plants. The rooms downstairs were bare and cold, and furnished with coat stands and folding chairs. The largest room, where the pupils gave their concerts, was equipped with a stage and a grand piano.

Madame Lola was greatly respected. Students and staff thought of her as she thought of herself—as a dedicated woman of high ideals and frail health. Gales of hearty laughter, clumping footsteps or the smell of fish and chips being consumed in the rest room were apt to bring on one of Madame's spells. (In England, "rest room" is not a euphemism. It means what it says: a room with chairs— usually sofas and armchairs—for resting.) In the enforcement of discipline, few women have used the small headache to greater advantage than Madame Lola. On the slightest provocation, Madame would retire to her dimly lighted bedroom, there to lie motionless on a chaise longue until either the offending student had been reduced to tears, or her secretary had tiptoed in with soothing words, bringing China tea and lemon on a little lacquer tray. Madame's spells could pass off just as quickly as they came, but it was amazing how many tiresome problems they solved. Students and staff did not like to be awkward when poor Madame Lola was not feeling well.

Madame Lola's husband (his name was Frank Beggs) traveled in shampoo. Frank was fifteen years younger than his wife—a round, jolly man, with a head of thick, beautifully wavy chestnut hair. Because of his work, he was away from home a great deal, and his frequent comings and goings were an emotional strain on everybody at the school. Mr. Beggs inspired in his wife a kittenish air which never failed to enchant him. ("I'll give you one teeny guess, Frankie, what I did while you were in Bunster." "Something artistic, pet, I'll be bound. Something artistic!")

The Chesterfield School of Voice employed a staff of three: Miss English, the secretary, Miss Newey, the accompanist and Nancy, the maid. The three women were devoted to Madame, and shouldered all the household chores and routine business with the exception of the students' bills. With these, Madame needed no help at all—she was as alert with them as a squirrel is with nuts.

Derbyshire girls marry young, and as brides they quickly lose interest in self-improvement. Madame Lola had, therefore, to work fast: her customers judged by results. All day long she criticized, admonished, sighed—the school echoed with her cries of disapproval. Her praise was so hard to come by that it was a wonder her students did not give up the struggle altogether, and perhaps they would have if the fees had been less exorbitant, and not payable in advance.

The school's curriculum of weekly private lessons was studded with musical afternoons and at homes. Madame Lola gave a great many of these—admission was by gilt-edged invitation card. On such occasions, the large downstairs room was crowded with the performers' relatives and friends, and with the school's past pupils, who, although they had now neither the time, money nor inclination to continue their own studies, welcomed the chance to dress up and go to a party. After the music (songs and recitations) tea would be served in the back rehearsal room, with Miss English pouring and Miss Newey and Nancy passing cake. If Frank was home, he would attend too, beaming and shaking hands with everyone, his flashing smile and glossy appearance (Frank always looked as if he had stepped out of an advertisement for a dry-cleaning establishment) adding considerably, in Madame's opinion, to the stylishness of the afternoon. A regular feature of Madame Lola's at homes was the presentation of certificates of merit. Every student who left the Chesterfield School of Voice was presented with a large piece of evidence, suitable for framing, that Madame Lola was completely satisfied with the girl's progress and achievements. For its size, the Chesterfield School of Voice must have given away more pasteboard than any other educational institution in England.

When Gladys arrived at Madame Lola's on the last Saturday of 1912, it was as if a tender young carrot had been transplanted to a hothouse. She was the youngest pupil by several years, and she exceeded all of them in her rawness, her eagerness to learn, the promise of her voice and the hopelessness of her appearance—Gladys never could keep her stockings pulled up straight or her hair tidy. She seemed to Madame Lola to offer limitless possibilities, of the kind that the blank canvas offers the artist, or a block of fresh marble the sculptor.

"We are going to have a beautiful time together, you and I," Madame said softly, with a flutter of her heavy eyelids, when Gladys finished her first song (for safety's sake, she had chosen "O for the Wings of a Dove" again). "Miss English will give you a new white notebook, and in it we will write down your exercises."

These exercises, it turned out, were all directed at Gladys' speech. Fortunately Madame Lola did not know enough to tamper with Gladys' singing voice, but her Derbyshire accent, penetrating as a saw, offered unlimited scope. Gladys was ordered to practice vowel sounds in front of a mirror, and to stop using the words "thee" and "thou."

Gladys tried. She practiced conscientiously, day after day, and every Saturday she made the long, cold journey to Chesterfield alone. She never missed a lesson or was late for it, she memorized quickly, and she almost never forgot what she was told. Her diligence deserved reward, and she would soon have become Madame Lola's star pupil had it not been for a problem that defied both child and teacher. Instead of being awed, as the other students were, by the elegancies of her new surroundings, Gladys found everything connected with the Chesterfield School of Voice uncontrollably funny.

In the middle of a student concert, a musical afternoon, or even during the solemn business of the presentation of certificates of merit, an unrestrained guffaw might burst upon the audience's astonished ears. Afterward, even before Madame Lola was prostrate upstairs on the chaise longue, Gladys would be abject with apology.

"I do my best to keep it in, Madame, but once I feel it coming on, nothing don't do no good."

"Nothing *helps*, dear. Nothing helps!"

"Nothing helps. It's like a sneeze. You know—it sprays all out."

Madame Lola tried everything—scolding, cajoling, tears and many, many headaches. Nothing did any good because Gladys was already trying. Sometimes several concerts would pass without any embarrassing interruptions, and then, just as Madame was feeling free to relax, they would occur again. The only remedy seemed to be to exclude Gladys from performances at which guests were present, but this would also have meant excluding from the program the best voice the school had. Even the faithful Frankie was no consolation. "Kid's a yell," he would say. "Plain as a maypole, and yet when she gets up there on the platform, I can't look at anyone else."

Actually, Gladys' behavior at the school was exemplary when compared with the way in which she carried on at home. The Miller family could hardly wait for Saturday night to hear about their sister's latest lesson. All of them thought Madame Lola's efforts to turn their Gladys into a lady the funniest thing they had heard. "I'm to say *hiou dew dew* now when I meet folks," Gladys announced one evening. "What d'you think of that, Mum? Hiou dew dew!"

The little sisters jumped up and down. "Hiou dew dew!" they cried. "Hiou dew dew!"

2

MADAME LOLA loved special occasions. Christmas, New Year's, St. Valentine's Day, Easter, Midsummer, Harvest, and Halloween were elaborately celebrated at the School of Voice, but the biggest party of all was in July, when Madame had a birthday. On that day, first thing in the morning, the local florist moved into the school with green wooden tubs containing little trees, and tall jars of stiffly wired flowers. The trees were set in the entrance hall and down the sides of the big classroom, and the flowers were arranged so that the little stage resembled a bower. Madame's presents—perfume, candy and baskets of fruit—were placed on a long table, and all morning the staff ran about breathlessly gathering up fallen tissue paper and wrapping ribbon. At the students' concert in the afternoon, Madame Lola presented the birthday scholarship, an award that entitled the recipient to a year's free lessons. After the concert, there was tea, and the next day the school closed for six weeks so that Madame could rest at the Spa Hotel, Matlock, while Miss English, Miss Newey and Nancy gave the building its annual cleaning.

There was usually a good deal of speculation among Madame Lola's students about the birthday scholarship award, but in July, 1913, the matter was hardly discussed at all; Gladys Miller seemed to everyone to be the obvious choice. Gladys' grant from the New Cut Miners' Welfare would end with the school year, and while Madame very much wanted her to continue her lessons after that, Gladys could not possibly afford to pay her own way. Nobody resented this situation; all the girls liked Gladys. Her voice was something they could boast about, and she was too young to offer them competition in the only field where competition mattered to them. At thirteen years old, few girls are seriously concerned with the acquisition of a husband.

Several of the students even tried to help Madame Lola by doing a little cultivating to the raw carrot themselves.

"There goes your blouse again, popping right out of your skirt," Nellie Wayne, a Chesterfield girl, complained. "Come here and let me fix it for you."

"Thanks, Nellie. I got a piece of tape for that at home, but I forgot to put it on."

"And your hair." This from Violet Jakes, whose father owned a farm near Tibshelf. "Why'n't you slick it over? Looks like you just been out in a high wind."

"Well, I have. It was blowin' clobbers when I left home."

The name of the winner of the birthday scholarship was supposed to be kept secret until Madame herself announced it during the festivities, but Holly and Fred were told, and they were, of course, tremendously pleased. The Miller family were bad at keeping good news from each other, and all the children knew that there was something exciting in the wind connected with a letter from Madame Lola that Fred and Holly kept reading to each other and hiding from them. When, however, they heard that they were all to attend the birthday concert, their curiosity was superseded by excitement. Holly sewed the girls new dresses; Fred's Sunday suit went to the cleaners.

Gladys could very easily have found out about the birthday award if she had thought to ask, but the truth was she was becoming thoroughly tired of secrets. The Chesterfield School of Voice was full of them. Did you hear what happened to Lucy on the paddy train? Do you know what Madame Lola said to Nellie Wayne? Have you seen the valentine Violet's Cecil sent to Julie Cook? "No, I haven't. And what's more, I don't want to," Gladys had said.

The other girls laughed. "That's because you're only a baby still," they told her. "You'll mind like anything later on. Julie getting Violet's valentine! I never!"

Madame's birthday was on a Saturday and, as Gladys had to attend a rehearsal at the school that morning, she left Tor by her usual bus, leaving the rest of the Millers to follow in the buggy they had hired for the occasion. The rehearsal dragged, and so, Gladys thought, did the lunch that followed it—Madame Lola provided the performing artistes with a meal of sandwiches, cake and milk. When this was over and the girls were leaving the kitchen to change into their party clothes, Nancy drew Gladys to one side.

"It's so crowded in the rest room with all the others," she said. "Why not use my room? It ain't big, but at least you'll have it to yourself."

Gladys was Nancy's favorite pupil, always singled out for small favors—the piece of cake with the cherry on top, the creamiest glass of milk.

"Oh, Nancy, may I? That *is* nice. With only one mirror for all of us, you know how it is."

Nancy's bedroom was in the basement, a tiny cell separated by a partition from Madame Lola's trunk room. It was very neat and clean, with an iron bedstead, a scrubbed yellow bureau, and pictures of the Virgin and of Madame Lola facing each other from opposite walls. Nancy helped Gladys to dress. She had not intended to mention the birthday scholarship, but in the coziness and privacy of her small familiar quarters, the temptation proved too great. Once the news was out, she added her own comment: "My, but you're bright! I bin around this place more years than I care to say, and I've never known a kid your age make such a hit with Madame."

Gladys swung round and hugged her.

"Nancy, Nancy! When'll I be given it? How soon? Just think what Mum and Dad'll say!"

"Stand still, for the Lordy's sake, while I get these buttons did up. Now give your hair a real good brushing."

"Never mind my hair. I *must* tell Nellie and Violet."

The quickest way from Nancy's bedroom to the students' rest room was by a corridor that ran under the stage between the side entrance to the school and the back stairs. Gladys took this, and in the darkest part of it she ran straight into Frank Beggs.

Frank's mind was full of worries. He had been away for three days and was already late home for his wife's birthday. He had brought her a different pair of earrings from the ones she had asked him for, and he still had to change his clothes before the concert. Suddenly he found himself with a dazzling young girl in his arms. She wore a white dress whose brightness seemed to light up the dark passage, and she had flying long black hair and dancing eyes. She babbled something to him but he did not hear what it was. He put his mouth quickly over hers.

The girl (he realized now that it was Gladys Miller) responded at once, warmly, and nestled delightfully against him. When he released her, she cried: "I knew you'd be pleased!" and smiling gaily, darted off up the stairs.

Madame Lola's birthday concert was always a painful experience. The students, in their white dresses, black stockings and black buckle shoes, sat self-consciously on gold chairs on the stage, facing an audience just as uncomfortable as they were, also seated on gold chairs. Madame, in a dress of silver lamé on which red velvet flowers had been sewn, swept about the room, welcoming her guests and fussing over the pupils and staff. Frank Beggs followed his wife, smiling and shaking hands, and pausing every now and again to run his fingers through his carefully pomaded curls. Miss Newey and Miss English whispered crossly to each other behind the piano. Miss English had to turn the pages, and she never remembered from one year to the next exactly how soon this must be done. Out back in the kitchen, Nancy nibbled at the party food.

Nobody at the concert was more uncomfortable than Fred Miller. He found the atmosphere of the room too warm and the smell of the flowers and perfume too heady. Beads of perspiration stood out on his brow. The program appeared to be just as long as he had feared it might, and from where he sat, his view of the stage was partly obscured by two of the florist's little trees. He had a fine view of Gladys, however, and he thought she looked a treat. His four younger daughters, in their starched new clothes, sat stiffly between him and their mother—clean as little whistles, and for once too subdued to fidget. Even Holly, who had wanted so much to come, looked scared.

Once the music began, the audience, including Fred, felt better. The singing was vigorous, enthusiastic and lively. It was unfortunate that Madame Lola liked her girls to smile while they sang, and make meaningless gestures with their hands and arms, for when all sang together there was not enough room on the stage for these exercises, and as the sturdy young people hit each other, their smiles changed quickly to more understandable expressions. That lass next to our Glad, Fred thought, will be counting her bruises tomorrow.

The audience was subjected to "Cherry Ripe," "John Peel," "Caller Herrin'" and "Rule Britannia." Interspersed among these were recitations that seemed to Fred to have no purpose in beginning and no particular reason to end. Gladys was not allowed to recite (her speaking voice continued to elude all Madame's efforts to clip and flatten) but she was permitted one song alone. Holding a long-stemmed rose in one hand, which she waved about at intervals, she sang:

> Once a boy a rosebud saw,
> Rosebud in the heather;
> 'Twas so young and morning bright,
> Gaz'd he on it with delight
> In the sunny weather;
> Rosy, rosy, rosy bud,
> Rosebud in the heather.
> Wilful boy—he plucked the rose,

Rose amid the heather;
Rosebud tore his hands amain
Little boots his cry of pain,
In the sunny weather!
Rosy, rosy, rosy bud,
Rose amid the heather!

Finally, when it was long past Fred's usual teatime, the moment of the bestowal of the birthday award arrived. Madame Lola and her husband ascended the stage, and Madame made a speech. Then Gladys was called upon to receive a small pink envelope that Frank held in his hands.

She looked flushed and on the verge of tears as she stepped forward. Taking the envelope, she smiled and then, closing her eyes and parting her lips, she held up her face.

Madame was charmed. "She wants a kiss, dear," she said. Stiffly, Frank leaned forward until his mouth just touched the girl's forehead. Gladys rewarded him with a clear, companionable guffaw.

Fortunately, for once, she was spared her usual apologetic progression, for the audience was making so much noise applauding that nobody but Gladys and Frank heard. Gladys was much amused, and she would have told Nellie and Violet as much afterward if something Nellie said had not stopped her.

"I'll bet that's the first time Frank Beggs ever kissed a student slap in front of Madame! You'd better watch your step, Gladdie. Madame'll take away your scholarship if she catches you having Frankie's babies."

3

ON SUMMER evenings, if the weather was fine, the Male Voice Quartet, a section of the Tor and New Cut Glee Club, sang for an hour in the open air from the gibbet steps. They began around eight o'clock, a time that permitted the audience, as well as the performers, an opportunity to refresh themselves afterward at The Old Spot, The Midge and The Nag's Head. On quartet nights, Holly set a table outside the kitchen door of the inn and employed

Mrs. Dutton to sell lemonade and orange squash and penny bags of sherbet to the children. (In Derbyshire, sherbet is the name given to a sugary powder colored pink, yellow or green, that effervesces when placed on the tongue.) Most children are allowed to stay up late in summer, on any night it isn't raining.

The quartet performances were never advertised in advance—there was no need. Tor folk liked to spend their evenings outdoors whenever they could, and the customary walk was up to the village green and around the gibbet, so if there was a concert, people soon knew about it. The quartet was composed of four of the glee club's best singers, so the music was always worth hearing.

One Friday in August, 1913 (it was the day before the Miller family left for Skunby-on-Sea), Tor enjoyed a touch of this rare, fine weather. During the afternoon, the sun came out for several short spells, and the sky that evening was without a cloud. Gladys and her sisters hurried through their supper so as to be at the gibbet steps before the crowd. Children were permitted to sit at the feet of the singers: adults had to stand on the grass, or in the road.

Gladys found a vacant space two steps from the top, on the corner facing the school. She had a bag of potato chips on her lap, and she munched these contentedly while she listened. It was not difficult for the quartet to make itself heard—the audience was an attentive one, and the policeman, Bob Greenhaugh, stationed himself on the road and held up any traffic that there might be. Nobody objected to this, for none had business so pressing at this time of the day that it could not wait an hour if there was singing.

Tonight's program included an old favorite, an eight-stanza tale of which the first verse went as follows:

> Ther was a bonny blade,
> An' he marri'd a coontry maid,
> An' he safely conducted her home, home, home:
> She was neat and she was smart
> An' she pleased him to his heart,
> But eh! poor lassie, she was dumb, dumb, dumb.

Down in the crowd, their whippets standing quietly beside them, Gladys noticed Peter Micklem and Rabie Andrews. The expression of concentration on their faces reminded her of the time she had watched them from the corridor of The Nag's Head, late for work on the morning of her first lesson with Madame Lola. It seemed a long time ago. She had been worried then about whether or not she would succeed, but really, when you came down to it, success was easy. All you had to do was learn what was set before you, and then behave exactly as you pleased.

The quartet's leader was speaking to her. "Glad—want to join us in the next one?"

"I'm plumb full of potato chips, Mr. Emney."

"Never mind. It's a song you know."

"Go on up, Glad," a man called. " 'Tain't every day of the week that Len Emney asks a girl to sing with him."

" 'Tain't every day of the week, Harry, that I got a prize girl of Madame Lola's here *to* ask."

Gladys stood up and slowly brushed the potato crumbs from her skirt. Then she joined the singers, standing a little apart from them so that she could watch the leader. Softly, the men began:

> Early one morning, just as the sun was rising,
> I heard a maid sing in the valley below:

Gladys sang alone:

> Oh, don't deceive me: oh, never leave me!
> How could you use a poor maiden so?
>
> Oh gay is the garland, and fresh are the roses,
> I've culled from the garden to bind on thy brow,
> Oh, don't deceive me; oh, never leave me!
> How could you use a poor maiden so?
>
> Remember the vows that you made to your Mary,
> Remember the bow'r where you vow'd to be true,
> Oh, don't deceive me; oh, never leave me!
> How could you use a poor maiden so?

The men continued:

> Thus sang the poor maiden, her sorrows bewailing,
> Thus sang the poor maid in the valley below:

Gladys finished softly, as the last of the light faded:

> Oh, don't deceive me, oh, never leave me!
> How could you use a poor maiden so?

4

THE Millers' holiday at Skunby was even better in 1913 than it had been in 1912. From start to finish, the weather was perfect, and no time was wasted while members of the family decided what they most wanted to do—all knew, and plunged after their respective pleasures within five minutes of their arrival at The Dunes. Fred, by means of a carefully composed correspondence that had been going on since early spring, had managed to arrange his week's vacation to coincide with those of his bowling cronies of last year, while Holly had bragged so successfully about the amenities of the town and the beneficent effect of the sea air upon her children's health, that two other Tor families had come to Skunby too. The Crews had rooms above the Millers at Mrs. Pegler's, and the Tolmans (Reg Tolman was the Tor carpenter) were housed across the street.

Holly was enchanted to have some of her own neighbors with her—she liked a change of scene better than she liked a change of face. The Tor contingent played games on the beach together, shrieked at one another from the sand sailing boats, and screamed as they paddled in the chilly sea. With the exception of Fred, who was determined to have a restful holiday (when not playing bowls, he slept in a deck chair beside the bowling green) they kept on the go all day long.

Fred decided that the only occasions during the day when his womenfolk sat still were at meals and during the performances of the Young Christian Army and the Lansbury Larks. Blanche was Lost Sheep Officer this year; her job was to round up congregations for the Reverend Fox to preach at. The Millers found it less troublesome to attend the Young Christian services than to try to avoid Blanche, who operated as seriously as a newly appointed parks attendant faced with a lawn of loose orange peel.

Holly did not really need a holiday at all, and she throve on all this activity. She was beginning to put on weight (she laughed too much, Fred said) but, although she squealed with horror when she weighed herself on the pier and saw where the hand on the clock flew round to, she continued to eat just as much Skunby rock as her daughters, and she liked a dish of winkles to follow.

In whatever ways the families from Tor spent their day, the evening was always devoted to the Lansbury Larks. This year, except for Mae Lansbury and the pianist, Cookie, Joe Lansbury again had a new company, and he had increased its size by one. Instead of Eddie and Max, he had two very tall male dancers named Alec and Dick; Bettine had been replaced by a fat girl, Ella, who played the trumpet, and the addition to the company was a middle-aged Italian whose act consisted of encouraging a pair of poodles to jump through a hoop.

Although Joe was still far and away the most popular member of the Larks, Alec and Dick also had a following. They did soft-shoe dancing that fascinated their audiences, and they sang rapid little songs in voices as sharp and impersonal as a pair of evenly plucked guitars. Their best numbers were presented in the second half of the program, when the company changed from its pierrot costumes into evening dress. Then Alec and Dick, in tails, top hats, white gloves and monocles, and carrying tasseled canes, made fun of the gentry:

> I'm a funny sort of Johnny, I philosophize a lot,
> And when I think, I think a lot of thoughts;
> And when my brain gets addled, as the best brains always do,
> Well, I go and have a pick-me-up at Shorts.
> But nothing really ruffles me—I don't see why it should—
> Whatever comes along, I never cry;
> No, the only thing that worries me at all is simply this—
> I cannot keep my eyeglass in my eye.

There was also a sketch in which Joe Lansbury added his comments.

ALEC. I do feel seedy, dear old pally.
DICK. Really?
ALEC. Yaas.
JOE. Great Scott!
ALEC. I dressed today without my valet.
DICK. Really?

ALEC. Yaas.
JOE. Great Scott!
ALEC. You know, I always find it best,
   After the fag of getting dressed,
   To take at least an hour's rest.
DICK. Really?
ALEC. Yaas.
JOE. Great Scott!

As before, Gladys attended every performance that the Larks gave during the Millers' stay in Skunby except the one on the afternoon of Lily's birthday. That day, the family had tea at the Grand Hotel, and the meal was so elaborate and so slowly served that Gladys missed the Lark Walk as well as the afternoon pierrot show. As a result, she quarrelled with Lily and was banished to bed until suppertime, but even Holly had not the heart to make her miss the Larks' evening show.

"That kid's got pierrots on the brain," Fred complained. "You'd better do something before she goes daffy."

"All girls her age gets a crush on something," Holly said.

"They do? What did you 'ave?"

"Mr. Lakeman. Remember him? Bred canaries and sang like a woman."

"*Sang* like a woman! Blimey, Holly—"

"Yes, well, I know that now. So you just be thankful that with Glad it's pierrots, and let the child alone."

Gladys made a great nuisance of herself to the Lansbury Larks, but it was the kind of nuisance that the company throve on, and they were all very kind to her. They waved and smiled when they saw her waiting at the pier for a glimpse of them, they signed the photographs she asked them to sign, and there was a note of genuine regret in their voices when they refused her repeated requests for permission to visit them backstage. Joe regularly cracked his last year's joke about her being a long drink of water from that dry village, Tor, and even Alec and Dick, who were apt to keep themselves to themselves, gave her an occasional nod.

All this made Gladys very happy, though not so happy as she wanted to be. She longed for a chance to sing to Joe alone, and although she had asked him directly for this privilege more than once, no one was better able than Joe Lansbury to turn down requests in such a way that the inquirer was not really sure that she had made herself understood. What exactly Gladys expected would happen if she *did* sing alone to Joe was not clear—it had something to do with a job in the Larks, in which she would either share, or take over altogether, the role now being played by Mae Lansbury. Gladys did not lack self-confidence.

Joe frequently invited children up on the stage to sing with him, and whenever he did, Gladys, with her long legs, was the first to arrive there. But he never gave her a chance to show him what she could do alone, and when the small stage was full of other young enthusiasts, her voice was always drowned by theirs.

And then, two days before the end of the Millers' holiday, the opportunity Gladys longed for fell into her lap. Joe announced that on Friday night the Larks would stage a talent competition for children under fourteen. The first ten applicants to give their names in at the box office would be allowed to sing, dance or recite alone from the stage. The winner would be chosen by vote from the audience.

Gladys was the first to give in her name, and from then until the time of the competition the hours, even hours spent at Skunby-on-Sea, dragged interminably. On Friday evening, the Millers, the Crews, the Tolmans and the Peglers arrived at the pier theater nearly an hour before the performance was due to begin, and this time Fred bought everyone his own program. Holly, nervous for her daughter, said irritably to Gladys: "For Heaven's sake, fix your stockings so the seams don't wind."

The competition was held during the first half of the show, the last item before the intermission. Joe called the children up to the stage—there were three boys and seven girls.

"Well now," he said as he looked the group over. "Where'll we put our long drink of water this evening? You'd better go in the middle, lassie. Just cut that fat little boy in two."

Joe arranged the children in a line along the front of the stage, about a yard back from the footlights and well in front of the Lansbury Larks, all of whom, except Joe himself and Cookie, sat on tall white stools in a semicircle against the pink cotton back cloth. Cookie remained at his piano, but he shifted this a little so that he faced the children as he played.

None of the young artists had brought music with them, but with one exception Cookie knew the songs they sang, and if they danced, he watched their feet and played whatever seemed appropriate. Most of the children were very shy. The first boy was so stricken with fright that he could hardly produce a sound, and it was Joe rather than he who sang "I Do Like to Be Beside the Seaside." After him, two little sisters, dressed alike, recited "The Little Cares That Fretted Me," and followed it with a dance, accompanied by much flying of pale blue sash and hair ribbons. "Gentle Jesus, Meek and Mild," sung in a terrified voice by a chubby little girl, came next. Then it was Gladys' turn.

It was difficult to tell at this stage how the audience was reacting to the different performances; each child was given a generous reception. Gladys, however, was the only one who produced laughter, and this embarrassed her, for she was not, for once, trying to be funny. She had chosen one of Madame Lola's favorite numbers which she felt sure she sang well, but unfortunately the song, though extremely well known at the Chesterfield School of Voice, was completely new to Cookie. His stumbling accompaniment made Gladys go too fast. She was determined at all costs to fit in all the hand and arm motions, the smiles and nods of the head, with which Madame Lola had taught her to punctuate her performance, but taken at speed, the effect was that of a poorly controlled marionette:

> Sunshine glisten'd on the waters
> Of the little purling stream,
> Birds were singing in the tree-tops,
> Making life a pleasant dream;
> And at night the silv'ry moonbeams
> Floated on the calm, blue sky;
> Stars were shining o'er us, darling,
> Allie dear, o'er you and I.

Pompetty-pompetty-pom, went Cookie.

> 'Tis a year since last we parted,
> And I made you promise this:
> That you'd always love me, darling,
> Then I seal'd it with a kiss;

Part II

> May our life be one of pleasure,
> As it was in days gone by,
> May a sorrow ne'er o'ertake us,
> Allie darling, you and I.

Back in line again, scarlet from her exertions, Gladys noticed the laughter, but there was tremendous applause too, led by the seats occupied by the visitors from Tor.

Only one performer besides Gladys managed without some help from Joe. This was a ten-year-old girl named Posie Wheeler. Posie was very small for her age, very composed and very neat. She wore a brown velvet dress ("Velvet! In August!" Holly snorted to Fred), with a skirt that puffed out like a ballet dancer's, and pale pink socks above tiny white doeskin boots. Her thick brown hair was arranged in long, corkscrew curls, and she had a big white satin bow on the top of her head. In a voice as flat as a griddle Posie sang:

> Daddy wouldn't buy me a bow-wow, bow-wow,
> Daddy wouldn't buy me a bow-wow, bow-wow,
>   I've got a little cat,
>   And I'm very fond of that,
> But I'd rather have a bow-wow, wow, wow, wow, wow. . . .

When she finished, Posie curtsied slowly, without a smile. The applause was deafening.

Next, the vote was taken. Joe called each child forward, one by one, to receive the audience's applause. Each child was given an ovation, but much the greatest was reserved for Posie Wheeler.

A large number of the people on Skunby pier that night were from Derbyshire, and they knew something about singing. On that basis, and strictly speaking they should have voted on no other, Gladys should have won. But Joe Lansbury's audience was a holiday audience in holiday mood, and what caught their fancy was Posie Wheeler's looks. With her pale skin, her large somber eyes, and her incredibly neat clothes, she embodied for them their idea of what a good little girl should be, so unlike their own grubby, fidgety, unpredictable offspring. She seemed like something off a candy box or a magazine cover. If we clap enough, they thought, maybe we'll even get a smile out of her.

They did not. Posie heard their acclaim without showing any

sign of hearing it. She curtsied twice, very solemnly, and then accepted from Joe a kiss, a stuffed woolen dog and a large box of Gladys' favorite chocolate creams.

"Now we're for it," Fred grumbled to his wife. "Why'd we ever let Glad go in for this?"

The party from Tor, none of whom had expected anyone but Gladys to win, looked anxiously at the stage. Holly said: "It's the interval. Quick, Fred, get us some ice cream cornets."

One by one, the competitors climbed down from the stage and rejoined their parents. All except Gladys. When her turn came, she did not so much as look in the direction of her family, but ran down the side aisle, and out of the building.

Fred began to fuss. "Now what? Where d'you suppose she's gone?"

"Home, I expect. Just leave her be."

"'Leave her be!' There's a mother for you. How dost know our child ain't drownin'?"

"Fred Miller, for goodness' sake! If Glad hasn't learnt at her age not to kill herself over a disappointment, it's too late for you and me to teach her. Now where's them cornets?"

But Holly *did* hurry home as soon as the second half of the program was over—she almost ran down the pier and along the street that led to The Dunes. Gladys was home all right as she had expected she would be, upstairs in the big front bedroom that the Miller sisters shared. She was lying down, still in her clothes, her face hidden in her pillow.

Holly did not speak to her, but she had plenty to say to her other daughters as she poured them their milk in Mrs. Pegler's kitchen.

"None of you's to say a word to Glad—or to each other once you get upstairs, understand? And that goes particularly for you, Blanche. If I hear you sayin' your prayers tonight, you'll get one of the best spankings you ever had. And the Reverend Fox'll get one as well, I shouldn't wonder, first thing in the morning."

5

WHEN one is thirteen, trouble does not cause sleepless nights, or even restless ones. Gladys slept well. She awoke early, feeling hungry, and uncomfortable in her mussed clothes—Holly had made no attempt to undress her. It was a moment or two before she recollected where she was and what had happened. When she remembered, the weight that sleep had lifted from her slid heavily back into place. I am a failure, she thought, a complete failure, and there is nothing in the world that I can do about it.

There was, however, something she could do about her hunger. Holly had left a glass of milk on the table beside her bed, and with it a large red apple, and two cream-filled cookies. Gladys got up and carried these downstairs. She sat on the bottom step and ate them. Then, letting herself quietly out of the house, she walked down the road that led to the beach.

The tide was high. There was nobody about. Gladys climbed along the top of a groin of stone masonry that projected out into the sea, until she came to a place where she could sit and rest her back against a raised parapet. On one side, the water looked deep; it heaved with the incoming waves, and dragged at the seaweed which clung to the masonry. On the other side, the waves broke gently over a high mound of pebbles. When the water drained noisily backward, bubbles lay on the tops of the stones.

The wind blew Gladys' hair over her face and whistled through her clothes; the parapet was poor shelter. She shivered, although she was not really cold. Anyone seeing her doleful expression might have guessed the turmoil that her mind was in, although she had no intention whatever of throwing herself into the sea, as Fred had feared. What she was doing was forcing herself to become accustomed to a disagreeable idea—an unpleasant experience for a person of any age. Once I am *used* to being a failure, she thought, it won't be nearly so bad. It is this in-between stage that hurts. She tried to think of all the people she knew who had failed. Hiram Poole was certainly one, and look how many people there were who liked Hiram; he had a great many friends, even though he really did nothing except wave at them. I shall have to try and be like him—smile, and be nice to people. What a prospect! If only I had Posie Wheeler's body. But I never shall, I am too tall, and my legs are too long, and I'll probably be fat like mother the minute I am grown up. . . .

At that moment, Gladys became aware that her father was walking along the breakwater toward her. She smiled wanly at him (nothing like starting to be pleasant at once) and he sat down beside her. After a while, he said: "When I was a lad, I had a mind to farm. You know those meadows over the creek at Tibshelf, beyond Tibshelf Church?"

Gladys nodded.

"Them's the ones I dreamed about: pretty, grateful land. But I never got to farm, either there or anywhere else. I hadn't the strength. I came to The Nag's Head instead, and there I met thy mother. That couldn't have happened if I'd set myself up Tibshelf way."

"Dad. Are you telling me this because you think I was upset last night?"

"Maybe I am. Tha seemed upset. Just a mite."

Gladys got to her feet. Not even Fred could be allowed to feel sorry for her. "Creepers!" she said. "What's a prize, more or less? I'd like to have won, of course, but I don't *care*."

Fred got up too at that, relief in every muscle. He could not think of anything to say, so he said nothing, just took his daughter's hand, and led her back to the beach. As they walked toward The Dunes, he said: "Not a word about this. I'll be in trouble with thy mother if it's thought I came out looking."

The Millers were already at breakfast, and the four younger sisters looked anxiously at Gladys when she and Fred came in. No one spoke. Holly served the latecomers, and then said sharply: "What's come over everybody? Hasn't no one in this family a tongue?"

6

The village school in Tor closed its doors for the month of August and reopened them again on the first Monday of September. The teachers, Mr. Gillingham, old Miss Piper, and Miss Piper's niece, Miss Ethel Piper, were always glad to start work again, for none had anything much to do during vacations. Unfortunately the education offered in Tor was not of the highest quality. Mr. Gillingham, the principal, was a gentle, forgetful, near-sighted man, and the Pipers, although they had prodigious memories, and were bottomless receptacles of local gossip, were no good at all at maintaining discipline. In the daily battle between the teachers' mild intention to teach and the pupils' determination not to learn, it was usually the pupils who won, for their parents took no interest in what they did during school hours. Tor had no P.T.A., no school clubs or societies, no report cards and no athletic program; it had only the law, which forced every child between the ages of five and fourteen to attend school and, having seen to it that its children obeyed the law, Tor considered its responsibilities toward their education discharged.

The situation would have been more sad than it was for Mr. Gillingham and the Pipers if they had expected anything different, but they did not. They took their work easily, and when the day was done, Mr. Gillingham retired to Mrs. Gillingham and the butterfly collection he had started when he was eight, and the Pipers bustled away to their small, furnished rooms, where they brewed pots of tea and picked over the local news together.

With the exception of Blanche, who applied herself assiduously to everything she did, the little Millers were poorer students than most. Books were not part of the furnishings of their home; indeed the Millers *had* no books except a Bible and a manual or two on rabbit breeding. Holly never read to her children because she never read to herself, unless one counted a few minutes on Sundays with the picture section of Fred's newspaper. Blanche's good standing at school, therefore, was a surprise to her parents. At the age of eleven, she was quicker than her father at arithmetic, and she often gave him a hand with The Nag's Head accounts.

To Gladys, school in September, 1913, was very wearisome indeed. Her fourteenth birthday was not until the following May, and only then would she be able to finish lessons for good. Boredom was a new sensation to her, and she did not care for it. Even her classes at the Chesterfield School of Voice had begun to lose their charm. Madame Lola, for some reason, had suddenly become unpleasantly strict. Now, when Gladys guffawed, or said "thee," or forgot to polish her shoes, Madame no longer reproved her, or withdrew with a headache to the chaise longue. She handed out punishments instead. When Gladys' words were not pronounced in the way Madame liked to hear them (clipped of all their flavor, and as lifeless as Posie Wheeler's singing) Gladys was forbidden to talk to the other students for the rest of that day. When she burst out laughing in the middle of a rehearsal, she was made to eat lunch by herself, and once, when Madame Lola caught her imitating the way Frank Beggs bowed to callers, there was talk of withdrawing the birthday scholarship. This threat did not alarm Gladys as much as Madame Lola had hoped it would, for it was becoming increasingly apparent to the present holder of that honor that the birthday scholarship called for a standard of behavior far beyond Gladys Miller's powers.

Not only Madame Lola had changed. Frank Beggs was not the same either. He did not even seem to remember who Gladys was. When they met, which was not very often, he would nod distantly and hurry by without a word, as if his memory was no better than that of poor Mr. Gillingham, with whom Gladys had never been on kissing terms. Gladys remarked on Mr. Beggs' failing memory to a new student, Wendy Roberts, a pretty blonde girl, rumored to be rich. "Why, Gladys Miller! What a thing to say!" Wendy exclaimed. "Mr. Beggs isn't forgetful. He isn't happy, that's all. That Madame doesn't understand him."

"Do *you* understand him?" Gladys asked in surprise, but Wendy only gave her a sharp look, and walked away, the bangles on her wrists jangling.

But if Madame Lola was a trial to Gladys, it was nothing compared to the trial Gladys was to Madame Lola. It was that lady's belief that the reason why she had never been able to produce a singer of the first rank from among her pupils was because the raw material of which gifted singers are made had never been offered to her for training. Now it had. In young Gladys Miller she saw the possibilities of fame, not only for Gladys herself, but for Madame Lola and the Chesterfield School of Voice. That a first-class voice is not necessarily linked to good manners, poise or the capacity to control a hearty laugh was something that had never occurred to Madame Lola, and she devoted all the determination that had gone into the organization and establishment of her school to trying to persuade Gladys to behave. When every other approach failed, Madame fell back on bullying. This was not easy for her, for she was a sentimental woman as well as a foolish one, and she did not enjoy pouncing on Gladys all the time. But she knew she would get no help from The Nag's Head. She had found this out at her birthday concert, when she said to Fred: "If your little girl works hard, she may become a famous singer one day."

Fred's expression had not changed. "Fame don't signify, Ma'am," he had said. "All we want is for our lassie to 'ave fun."

A major problem where Gladys was concerned was her fondness for mimicry. This, in later years, was to stand her in good stead, and was the one thing she learned from the Chesterfield School of Voice. She could do a very pleasant sketch of Madame receiving guests at an at home, of Miss English trying to find a missing paper, and of Miss Newey fumbling with dropped music. None of these was actually as funny as Gladys' audiences thought they were, but the girls at Madame Lola's encouraged Gladys for the same reason that members of a family encourage family jokes—not because the jokes are funny, but because a family likes to laugh.

Every now and again, however, just when Madame Lola felt herself coming to the end of her unresilient tether, Gladys would reward her. At the 1913 Christmas concert, for instance, the child sang divinely, taking the descants to the school carols with care and sincerity, her voice pure as a lark. Afterward, Madame Lola took Gladys on one side and said to her: "If you would like to come over next Saturday as usual, dear, when the school is closed for the holiday, I shall be very happy to give you an extra lesson."

"Oh no, Madame, thanks all the same." Gladys' voice was firm. "Wild blue cows wouldn't get me over here next Saturday. That's Boxing Day, and yipee! We're all going to the Manley pantomime."

7

TOWARD the end of March, 1914, Madame Lola decided to make one last effort to rescue Gladys Miller. One cannot but commend her perseverance. She reasoned that it was too much to expect a child of thirteen to appreciate what the future might hold for her, particularly when she spent six days out of seven in an atmosphere in which music was looked upon solely as an amusement. The situation seemed, however, one that could still be remedied, and consequently Madame Lola wrote a letter to Holly and Fred making them an offer of greater magnitude than she had ever made to any student. She proposed to take Gladys into the Chesterfield School of Voice as a weekly boarder, with privileges that would include extra lessons and the supervision of all her practice time. Under this arrangement, Gladys would spend only two nights a week at home. "Your daughter needs greater discipline," she wrote, "as well as the constant companionship of those who really understand her musical needs. We at the Chesterfield School of Voice are prepared to do everything in our power to help Gladys if you will permit us. We know we shall be well rewarded. As for her regular schooling, I am sure an arrangement can be made for Gladys to attend the town school *here* until her fourteenth birthday. After that, we shall hope to have her with us full time."

Madame's letter reached The Nag's Head on a Saturday afternoon. Holly and Fred were alone, finishing a tea of crumpets, seed cake, honey, sardines and homemade strawberry jam. Gladys was not yet home from Chesterfield, the two youngest Millers were at a birthday party, Lily and Blanche were roller skating in the lane. Fred was reading to Holly from the Manley *Reporter*, which this week included a special section describing a wool-processing plant that was being constructed in the Tor valley, on the Manley side of New Cut. There were photographs of the washing, dyeing and spinning rooms, and a portrait of the owner, a Mr. William Dade of Nottingham.

"Trade around here goes from good to better all the time," Fred commented. "Bring a lot more money into Tor, this will."

"And people," Holly said. "Where they all going to live?"

"Says here Dade's plan to employ mostly women, so there may not be many new families move in. But you realize what this means to us, love? Jobs for all our girls when they want 'em, and good jobs too. Good pay."

"Well, fancy! That *is* nice. Though Glad won't be wantin' to go there. Madame Lola seems set on her doin' something with her voice."

Then Madame's letter arrived. Holly read it and promptly burst into tears.

"Come now," Fred said, "where's thy pride? This is an honor."

"But Glad's such a baby, Fred! Lord's sakes, she's only thirteen."

"Mr. Hay was tellin' me he went to boarding school when he was eight."

"Mr. Hay's a nob. Nobs do that to their kids—we don't. I don't want Glad leavin' home."

"Then tell Madame Lola no."

"Shall I?"

"Well—" Fred paused. "Babies have to grow up, Holly. Ours same as anyone else's. I don't want Glad to go away any more'n you do, but it's got to be, sometime. You wanted her to have her voice fixed up."

"Oh yes, and I still do. And I know Madame Lola's a fine teacher."

"Well then. Glad'll work harder over there, I reckon, than she do here. She don't seem to practice the way she did."

"That's true. Time was when she worried about wasting money. Now that Madame Lola's payin' instead of the Welfare, she don't seem to care nearly so much."

Fred read the letter again. "Glad'll be beside herself when she hears," he said.

Holly dried her eyes. "Shall I tell her, or will you?"

"Let's let her read it for herself."

But when Gladys came home, she already knew about Madame's offer. She was certainly beside herself, but it was not with happiness. She was so angry she was hardly coherent.

"So when I couldn't see anything to smash," she shouted at her parents, "I ran out of the place as quick as I could, and slammed the door. I hoped the glass panels would bust—Madame loves that stained glass—but they didn't, though the shades fell off. I come home without my galoshes."

Holly said: "It don't matter one bit about them, dear. You sit up to the table before you tell us any more, and have your tea."

Later (the other children were home by then, and crowding round to hear) Gladys explained what had happened. It seemed that Madame Lola had been unable to wait for Holly and Fred to break the good news. She had told Gladys herself that morning. She outlined the program planned for Gladys' future studies—a dismal routine of lessons, practicing, rehearsals, performances, more lessons and more practicing, which left little time for meals and, so far as Gladys could see, none at all for play. Gladys had, however, been prepared to go through with all of it if Madame and her parents wished, but then Madame, carried away with her own enthusiasm, said: "The reason why we particularly want to have you here to live with us, dear, is that you are growing up, and Tor isn't the right environment for you any longer."

Gladys did not know the meaning of the word "environment," but she understood at once what Madame Lola meant, and it cut right at the roots of the family feeling that Holly had been at such pains to foster in her children.

"You mean my family ain't good enough?" she asked.

Madame Lola was flustered. She made incoherent excuses, ending with "You'll understand better when you're older."

Gladys said: "I understand right now. I can't think why I didn't see it before. You know something, Madame? You are absolutely no crackety good at all. You and your school remind me of a rotted beer keg."

Madame Lola's eyes seemed to pop out of her head. "I have never—I have never—!" she began.

"Creepers, creepers! Then it's more'n time you had! . . ."

Fred said: "You was terribly rude. She'll 'ave to write a letter of apology, won't she, Mother?"

"She'll do no such thing." Holly was almost as angry as Gladys by this time. "She'll 'ave no more to do with Madame Lola, and no writing to her neither. My poor baby! Well, I must say I'm glad you're all done with that place, lovey. I always said Madame Lola was no teacher, didn't I, Fred?"

But Gladys was not satisfied. She threw herself into her father's arms. "I acted bad, I know I did," she sobbed, "and I'll probably go to Hell when I die, because if I got the chance I'd do just the same again. Oh Dad, what's going to become of me? What shall I do?"

Fred stroked her hair. "Tha cannot do better than thy mother did," he said softly. "Stay home here at the inn, and when some right handsome fellow comes along, tell him he may marry thee."

8

DADE's woolen mill opened for business on the first of April. The plant consisted of three buildings, each several stories high, which bridged the river at a point east of New Cut where the Thorne ran through a small gorge. Dade's employed some two hundred women and girls, and in mid-May, the day after her fourteenth birthday, Gladys started work there as a junior washer.

The job of the junior washers was to propel clots of raw wool along a tank, by means of poles. From the washing room, the clots passed down a ramp into bleaching sheds. The water in the washing tank was very hot and full of strong-smelling soap, and this, mingled with the odor of the chemicals next door, created an atmosphere that was pungent as well as steamy to work in. The work was not hard, but it had its problems, chief among them being keeping dry. The girls wore wooden clogs, waterproof caps and coveralls, and they learned to eat their sandwich lunches very fast—Dade's had no cafeteria or lunchroom.

In spite of these drawbacks, however, the junior washers, none of whom was over sixteen, loved their work. Their backs and legs ached the first week, but after that they became used to the standing and stretching, and although they had less time now to call their own than they had had when they were in school, they felt as independent as sparrows. The washroom supervisor, a Nag's Head customer of long standing, was a kindly man, very easy to please. He let the girls chatter while they worked, and now and again he would send them off for a few minutes, one at a time, to sit outside, where the air, though not really fresh, at least did not smell as bad as it did inside.

Gladys worked at Dade's from seven o'clock in the morning until three in the afternoon, five days a week (because of their age, the junior washers worked shorter hours than the rest of the factory). With nobody to correct her accent, reprove her for laughing loudly, or order her to pull her stockings up, she found life sweet indeed. She still sang. As often as not, she took the soprano solo in the anthems at Tor Church on Sundays, and Mr. Emney had already invited her to appear as a "speciality" item with the Tor and New Cut Glee Club at a concert they were to give at the Miners' Welfare in July. Whatever Madame Lola and Joe Lansbury's audiences might think, it was consoling to Gladys to know that the people in Tor and New Cut liked to hear her sing.

But on the whole, her life was not greatly changed by leaving school and becoming a wage earner. She continued to share a bedroom with her four younger sisters, and to live in much the same way that they did. Fred told her that now she had her own pay envelope, she should give Holly something for her bed and board, but Holly would not hear of such an arrangement, and so every Friday night, the envelope, just as it was, was dropped into a shoebox at the back of the bar counter, there to stay until somebody in the family could think of a good use for it.

It was really a fine way to grow up, and a much happier one than Gladys would have enjoyed if, instead of being born Gladys Miller, she had been born Gladys Leake. The young Leakes, at Gladys' age, were packed off to boarding school, a world exclusively feminine, expensive and unwed. Their curriculum, hard study alternating with violent exercise, allowed only such time for eating, sleeping and elimination as was considered compatible with aggressive good health, with the result that when, at the age of eighteen, they emerged from this training, they were permanently stamped with the marks of it: they were brainy, brave and as sexless as bedsprings.

Gladys, however, was allowed to grow gently, surrounded by men and animals, as well as women. Nobody expected her to study like a man, or play games like one, or jump about in a gymnasium, or get up in the morning to the clang of a bell. Because she had a job, her life was, of course, subject to discipline, but the disciplines were all of a leisurely, unharassing kind. Dade's mill, like the village of Tor, did not do things in a hurry.

The junior washers, all of whom lived in Tor, walked to and from the factory together every working day. As they walked, they sang, their arms linked and their clogs splashing through any mud puddles there might be. The group's general lack of refinement would have horrified Madame Lola, and when Gladys told them this, in a neat imitation of Madame's accent and manner, the girls shrieked and begged for more. Their behavior reminded Gladys of the students at the Chesterfield School of Voice, but with one difference. Some of the older washers envied her.

"Saw you at the dance Saturday, Gladdie," Ellie Jones, who was sixteen, said one day. "Bert kiss you when he took you home?"

"Oh, yes. And so did Harry, earlier on."

"He never! I don't believe it."

"Suits me."

"Glad's going to be Dade's sy-reen before long," another washer said.

"Sounds to me she's one already." Ellie had walked home from the dance with her sister.

"Well, I don't know—" Gladys pondered this suggestion. "I ain't one for the dark doorways some of the boys like. I never was. What can't be done in the light of a street lamp don't get done, if it's me."

9

IN JULY, in a tremendous downpour of rain, Margaret Leake became the wife of Lieutenant Smalley-Rivers of the Gloucestershire Regiment. The event kept the Leake family, and indeed a large part of the population of Tor, busy for weeks—nearly everything for the wedding, including Margaret's trousseau, was made at home. A great marquee was erected on the lawn in front of the big house and, in accordance with traditional custom, a beer keg was set up in the stables, so that the extra help engaged to put the marquee up, move furniture about and prepare the elaborate wedding breakfast, could toast the bride's health while they worked.

In the normal way of things, Lady Leake hardly ever entertained.

For months, her only dinner guest would be the rector. Family baptisms, weddings or funerals, however, were always observed by the Leakes with lavishness. No expense was spared. Invitations to Margaret's wedding were sent out to every living member of the Leake clan, and even to one or two who were dead, whose names had not yet been scratched off in Lady Leake's address book. The clan, which was large and not at all close (its members rarely communicated with one another) accepted Lady Leake's summons almost without exception: only those stationed overseas, or hopelessly bedridden, declined. Their convergence upon Leake Revel merely added to the confusion in which Margaret Leake was living—her education, of course, having done nothing to prepare her for the limelight in which she now found herself. To the Leakes, it was both proper and natural for a young girl who had lived in quiet seclusion all her life suddenly to occupy the center of the stage, and to be responsible not only for the happiness of a husband, but also the care of a home, servants, large quantities of jewelry, furniture, silver and glass, and enough monogrammed linen to last a lifetime. Fortunately Margaret was an adaptable girl and very much in love. She followed her mother's advice in all things, and smiled sweetly on all the house guests who filled up her home. Luckily, the pronounced Leake family likeness made it easy for her to guess correctly who, though not always precisely which, each was.

Margaret's brother, Jamie, who seemed able to treat his Swiss sanatorium more as if it were a hotel than a hospital, came home for his sister's wedding, and gave the bride away. Jamie was now fifteen, a slight, quiet boy with a charming smile. Perhaps because her son was away from home so much, Lady Leake spoiled him— Jamie could do anything he wanted, even to the extent that, had this been his wedding rather than Margaret's, he would probably have been allowed some say in its arrangements.

Margaret and Hugh Smalley-Rivers had none. They exerted no more control over the ceremonies than do the brides and grooms in other primitive societies, anywhere else in the world. Hugh Smalley-Rivers, a serious young man, neat as a pin, realized early in the proceedings that handling any problems there might be later on in his married life would be child's play compared to the strain of the nuptials themselves. Just now, the survival of the two of them was all that really mattered.

It distressed Margaret to find that an essential part of the wedding arrangements was the transformation, almost beyond recognition, of the two buildings in Tor that she loved most, her home and her church. The insides of both were smothered in flowers, and the outsides decked with striped awning. Even the familiar ground was partly covered over: under the marquee on the Leake Revel lawn, a wooden floor was laid down, and on it were placed quantities of hard wooden chairs, with WORBOYS FOR WEDDINGS stamped on their undersides. The little sunken flagged path that led from the lane to the church door was also hidden—under a heavy, badly worn strip of red carpet, that bent up at the edges because it was too wide.

The Leakes were a reserved family except during weddings. Then they really let themselves go, submitting their young to a ritual that was at once religious, bawdy and historic. Martin Hay did what he could to persuade Lady Leake to accept a shortened form of the service ordained by the Church of England for the solemnization of matrimony, but she insisted on having everything there was, and so Margaret and Hugh, standing innocently in Tor Church before God, the rector and a great company of craning relatives, were briskly informed that marriage is not an enterprise to be entered upon unadvisedly, lightly or wantonly, to satisfy men's carnal lusts and appetites, like the brute beasts that have no understanding. It is for the procreation of children who are to be brought up in the fear and nurture of the Lord, and as a remedy against sin and fornication, that such persons who have not the gift of continency may keep themselves undefiled.

Hugh Smalley-Rivers, whose prominent chin was shaved so close that it looked about to bleed, stood stiffly at attention throughout this sound advice, his brow devoutly puckered. Margaret, struggling against the strong aroma of mothballs that clung to the ancient lace veil she was wearing (it is the custom in the English church for the bride to keep her face covered until the ceremony is over), moved suddenly a step away from her beloved, thinking, My God, what have I got myself into? It was, of course, far too late to worry about that now. Martin's peroration switched to include her: "Wives, submit yourselves unto your husbands . . . for the husband is the head of the wife. . . . Ye wives, be in subjection to your own husbands . . . even as Sarah obeyed Abraham, calling him lord. . . ."

Margaret's heart began to race, and it was Gladys Miller who calmed her. Gladys was sitting at the western end of the front row of choir stalls, a position that gave her an uninterrupted view of the bride. To Gladys, she embodied all the romance and wonder that a bride should inspire, although in actual fact Margaret was looking far from her best. Her wedding dress, made by Miss Gaines, a Tor farmer's daughter who had sewn for the Leake family for twenty years, was made of heavy, embossed satin, and as this material was too heavy to drape well, Miss Gaines had cut it plain, like a kimono, and added a wide, silver-cloth sash. The result was that Margaret, hot with the weight, looked a little like a rolled-up table napkin that has been squeezed through a silver ring.

Gladys thought: This is the way I shall have everything when I'm married—lace, and white satin, and orange blossom, and the full choir, and all the flowers I can lay my hands on. Everybody in Tor will come and look at me, and afterward we'll have a party too, with maybe a marquee over The Nag's Head yard.

With her mind so delightfully occupied, it is not surprising that when Gladys sang the anthem solo about hope and blessedness and love, she was able to convey a sense of peace to Margaret. Gladys' voice rose calm and strong into the roof of the little church, and after a few moments, Margaret moved back again, so that the sleeve of her gown touched Hugh.

After the ceremony, which was held at ten o'clock in the morning, the wedding guests streamed back to Leake Revel, and crowded into the marquee. There, a large slow meal was served, and several of Margaret's uncles and cousins made speeches, laced with little jokes. The humor of these embarrassed the bride and groom, but they went down extremely well with the bride's mother. During recent weeks, Lady Leake had been laboring under a strain quite as great as Margaret's. Her reputation with the Leake family rested on this wedding, on its organization, its liberality and on the quality and quantity of its champagne. Lady Leake had had to see to everything, with no husband to guide her, and she had succeeded. Nothing had been overlooked. Only one detail remained, and that was the traditional responsibility of the best man.

He did not fail her. When Margaret and Hugh were at last permitted to escape, they were pursued down the wet driveway by a bevy of young men pushing an ancient baby carriage. Lady Leake's

Part II 95

peals of appreciative laughter at this gesture were audible to the young couple even above the noise of Hugh Smalley-Rivers' brand-new Ford.

But if Margaret and Hugh disliked their wedding, a large number of other people enjoyed it very much, among them Margaret's younger sister, Catherine. As chief bridesmaid (she had been accompanied by five cousins) she had received much more attention than normally came her way, as well as a handsome diamond pin. Catherine was now seventeen. With Martin Hay's help, she had finally won the battle with her mother and was to be allowed to go to London in September to study medicine. Because of this she had a very soft spot in her heart for the rector.

"You don't look as if you cared much for weddings," she remarked to Martin, as they stood at the marquee entrance together, after the bride and groom had left.

"I've seen more of them than you have," Martin said.

"Yes, but after all, you do get paid. Is it true that you got an enormous fee from Mother for marrying Margaret and Hugh?"

"Enormous, yes."

"How much?"

"Are you any good at anagrams?"

Catherine stared. "I think so. Why?"

"Then perhaps you can think of a word of five letters, beginning n-o-, and ending s-e-y."

10

By ONE o'clock, the wedding guests had either gone home or retired to their rooms. Jamie Leake would have liked some lunch—lunch, he thought, might make Leake Revel seem more its usual self, which at present it certainly was not—but none was provided. The house and garden, usually so silent, were busy with people packing things up. The marquee was already half down, the potted plants were being loaded onto a cart, and Mr. Worboys' chairs were being stacked one upon another ready for their return to his shop in Manley, from which they had been hired. Most of the helpers were men, but some women were bustling about too, with trays of left-over food, wine glasses and china. One of these (she had a little girl with her) smiled gaily at Jamie, and he smiled back.

Jamie decided that he was in for a very dull afternoon. He walked over to the stable yard and took a look at his pony, but the pony, fussed by the general upset, did not seem particularly pleased to see him. He was wondering what to do next when a voice said: "You got a dog?"

Jamie turned round. It was the little girl. Indicating the pony, she added: "You let me ride him once, remember? I just wondered if you happened to have a dog."

"Well yes, I do. At least, I have a puppy. He's a whippet."

"They're the best. Have you trained him?"

"No. You see, I—"

"It takes two people."

The afternoon took on a brighter aspect at once. Lily Miller had never tried to train a dog before, but she did not tell Jamie that, and the puppy entered so rapturously into the proceedings that on more than one occasion her orders and his responses coincided. Jamie was impressed. At a quarter to four, when his mother came to find him ("You should have had a nap, dear. Good afternoon, Lily.") Jamie said: "Lily has a wonderful touch with animals, Mother. She is going to stay to tea with us."

Lily did not reach home until after five. "Such a tea, Mum! The most lovely eats, and she didn't have no pastry forks neither. We had a huge teapot, all silver and ruffles-like. Lady Leake said she hoped I'd come again."

"That was manners," Fred commented. "Don't think for a minute she meant it."

"Oh Fred!" Holly cried. "Don't be so mean. I'm sure you'll be asked again, lovey, if Lady Leake has time. How lucky you had your prettiest dress on."

"And clean panties," Gladys added amiably. "It was Lil's day for 'em, *if* she remembered."

Lady Leake was less enthusiastic. Over sherry that evening, she had an opportunity to consult her brother. Oliver Marshall was the only non-Leake house guest.

"What am I to do about Jamie?" she said. "I can't keep him at home. Switzerland is his only hope, at least for several years. But he has such odd notions, and no social sense whatever. Imagine it, inviting that little Miller girl to tea!"

"I liked her," Oliver said. "I like the Millers."

"I know you do. So does Martin. It doesn't matter now, of course, but I am thinking of later on. What am I to do if Jamie wants to *marry* a barmaid?"

"Just see to it that he picks a pretty one. What your family needs is fresh stock. I was only thinking in church today that it is more than time something was done about these Leake noses."

"What's that?" One of Lady Leake's brothers-in-law came abruptly into the room.

"The Leake roses," Oliver said.

"Ha! Know what you mean. An impressive sight, when you get a lot of 'em together."

After dinner at Leake Revel that night, bridge tables and a billiard foursome were arranged. Oliver did not play, and as his sister retired very early, he set off alone for a drink at The Nag's Head.

Oliver did not come to Tor very often. The neighborhood depressed him. He was a man who liked sunshine and a heated bedroom, neither of which one could be sure to find in east Derbyshire. He was an elderly man now, and something of a bore on the only subject that interested him—acting. He could talk on that topic by the hour, but it was not one that found a receptive public at Leake Revel, where his sister's in-laws, all of whom were bores too in the one field that interested *them,* looked with pity on any man who had never worn a uniform.

Buttoning his coat (he never came to Tor, even in July, without an overcoat) Oliver picked his way across Tor green, listening regretfully to the sucking noises his shoes made on the wet grass. It was not raining any more, but it was too late for any children to be playing on the gibbet steps, and these were deserted. Oliver stopped by the platform and then climbed up to look at the view. England enjoys a long twilight, and although it was nearly nine, it was not yet dark. Lights twinkled in several cottage windows, and the smoke from many small chimneys rose straight in the air, mingling with the grayness of the overcast sky. In this part of the world, Oliver thought, it must be very easy for a child to feel himself a part of history—everything he sees is the same yesterday, today, and (probably) tomorrow. On the other hand—Oliver descended the steps and continued his walk—these ancient surroundings might prove too dominating, make it difficult to pull up one's roots and settle elsewhere. Not that such a step seemed as necessary here as in some places. The usual incentives that young people have to leave the country for the town—better jobs, more amusement—did not seem to apply in Tor. The Halesowen Company, supplemented by Dade's mill, provided excellent jobs for everyone, and as for amusement, judging by the gales of laughter coming from The Nag's Head yard, this too seemed to be available close to home.

It was not, in Oliver's opinion, nearly warm enough to sit outdoors, but the white wooden seats in Fred Miller's garden were all occupied by the time he reached the inn. Some kind of entertainment was in progress on the front lawn. Oliver made his way into the saloon, which as usual was dark and quiet. Several brightly dressed New Cutters were standing along the bar (it was Saturday night) but most had taken their drinks outside.

"Why, Mr. Marshall!" Holly Miller hurried over. "A pint of light for Mr. Marshall, Rose, and in a pewter tankard. That's right, isn't it, sir?" Oliver nodded, warmed at once, as Holly intended him to be, by her cheerfulness and her good memory. "What a lovely wedding! I thought Miss Margaret looked ever so pretty—Mrs. Smalley-Rivers, that is."

"She looked all right, Holly, yes. Under-rehearsed, but all right. How's that fine baby of yours?"

"Growin' fast, sir. Flo'll be six tomorrow."

Oliver put a half crown down on the counter. "Take the beer out of that, and give the change to Flo in the morning with my compliments. How about the others?"

"Gradely, sir, thank you, I'm happy to say. Gladys is outside now. That's her, singing."

Oliver picked up his beer and took it into the garden. Close to the wall beside the lane, a group of mill girls and young miners stood singing in a semicircle in front of Gladys, their arms around each other's shoulders.

Gladys saw Oliver and stopped. "Mr. Marshall, sir! Anything special you'd like us to sing?"

"Thank you, no, Gladys. The regular program will suit me."

Gladys hesitated. There was no regular program. The group be-

gan calling suggestions: "Let's do 'By the Beautiful Sea' again."
Gladys shook her head.
" 'The River Hotel,' then?"
"No, I'm tired of that."
"Aw, come on, Glad! Make up your mind for the gentleman."
"Shall I do 'Madame Lola' again?"
"Yes!" Everyone applauded.

Oliver had never heard of Madame Lola, but by the time Gladys finished, he could picture her perfectly: the affected walk, the incredible speech, the awful emphasis on gentility. Gladys did not give a polished performance, but what she gave was true enough, and although it made Madame Lola out just as much of a fool as she was, Gladys' sketch was not unkind.

Next, Gladys started on "Abide with Me." During this, the members of her audience began to stroll back indoors. Only a few were still there with Oliver at the end.

Oliver said: "How often do you do this sort of thing?"

Gladys walked over to him. "Most Saturday nights, and sometimes at the mill, during the lunch break. Did I make you laugh with Madame Lola?"

"Yes, you did, though you oughtn't to have to ask that."

"Why not?"

"With a group the size of yours, and out of doors, you should know. You saw what happened to 'Abide with Me'?"

"Yes. I'm afraid I didn't sing it very well."

"You sang it very well indeed, but after Madame Lola, none of us was in the mood for a hymn."

Oliver took Gladys' arm and began propelling her toward the inn. "You have the makings of a very funny woman, Gladys, and that isn't at all a bad thing to be. But you must watch your audience. That's important."

Gladys did not understand what Oliver was talking about, but she was flattered to have his attention. She said politely: "Yes, Mr. Marshall. Thanks. I'll try."

Oliver pressed her arm. "Well, don't take my word for it. Try it yourself for a month and see."

Gladys beamed. "A month from today, I won't be here. Dade's is giving us junior washers a week off, and that's to be my week.

Dad and Mum and all of us are going to Skunby-on-Sea again."

But as it turned out, the Miller family stayed right where it was, and Gladys went on working. On the fourth of August, World War I began.

Part III

1

WORLD WAR I was the first war in English history which affected everybody in the country. No one was spared. Although the soldiers bore the brunt of the misery, the civilians, coping as best they might with the shortages, the air raids and the bad news, carried their share of the trouble. But while the war brought wretchedness to some, it brought advancement and sudden wealth to others. People spoke of the *nouveau riche,* a new social class that was trying to buy its way into the ranks of the aristocracy on the quick profits made in steel plants and shipyards (it was to succeed, but not yet). The war also made heroes. Amongst the latter, greatly to their own astonishment, were the coal miners of Tor and New Cut.

The press, in an effort to bolster morale on the home front, devoted a great deal of space to the civilian war worker. Nearly every day, there were pictures of armament makers at their benches, of women stitching uniforms or of black-faced miners returning from the pits. These men, in their tin hats and with their tea bottles protruding from their hip pockets, could have been photographed in the same pose at any time during the past two decades, but until the outbreak of war, nobody thought them newsworthy.

Tor accepted its place in the limelight philosophically. The men smiled obligingly into the cameras and when the results were published, they clipped them, and grinned, and nudged each other. It was no news to them that digging coal was dangerous work, or that it was vital to the British war effort.

The Halesowen colliery and Dade's mill went immediately onto overtime production. Both companies worked their employees long hours and paid them well, with the result that Tor became more prosperous than ever. Elsewhere in England, the shops grew emptier every day, but in Tor and in the other mining villages around Manley, there was plenty of everything. Indeed, except for the fact that there was no longer any icing sugar available for the tops of birthday cakes, the food situation in Tor during the war differed little from what it had been before the war began.

Tor was fortunate in other ways too. The village did not experience any air raids (aerial bombing was limited to the large cities and to the ports), and since all were already employed either in mining or farming, none of its menfolk were called up. The general effect of the war on Tor was therefore not one of strain, anxiety and separation, but busyness, self-importance and plenty. The fighting itself touched no one until, early in the summer of 1917, Leake Revel was turned into a wounded soldiers' convalescent home.

As soon as war broke out, Lady Leake had offered her house to the War Office, but her offer was refused because the army did not want to send wounded men to such a remote village. Lady Leake's generosity, however, was of a persistent kind, and by means of influential in-laws and nearly three years of needling, she wore the army down. Lady Leake at once moved out of her home into three rooms over the Leake Revel stables, and the wounded moved in. She was alone now. Margaret Smalley-Rivers was living in Gloucestershire, busy with babies and the Red Cross, and Catherine was in London, finishing the third year of her medical training. Jamie, who had returned to Switzerland two weeks before the outbreak of the war, could not come home until hostilities ceased.

Tor was delighted about the convalescent home. Offers to wash, clean and scrub poured into Leake Revel in a way that they had never done when it was Lady Leake rather than soldiers who needed domestic help. Although all the patients were convalescent, their injuries were such that many stayed in Tor for several weeks, and this gave the village time to make friends with a large number of foreigners—Welshmen, Scotsmen, Cornishmen and cockneys all found their way to Leake Revel.

The convalescent home accepted most of the local offers of help. Martin Hay was appointed chaplain, a job that he undertook in addition to his regular parish duties before he realized that it involved being entertainments officer as well. Amusing the patients was a problem: the hospital had only a few packs of cards, some jigsaw puzzles and a tiny library (Lady Leake had stored all her books along with most of the furniture that she could not herself use). Owing to the weather, even the men well enough to do so were rarely able to enjoy the outdoors. Martin was, however, extraordinarily successful in obtaining the services of concert parties. These troupes (they ranged in size from four for a small party, to

Part III

eleven for a large one) were essentially pierrots, though they did not wear pierrot clothes. They toured inland during the winter months, presenting much the same programs as the ones they gave in pierrot costume at the seaside in the summer. During the war, however, when the beaches were closed to tourists, the players who had not been called up stayed in concert party work the year round, performing to army camps and hospitals, as well as to civilians in the inland towns and villages. Because of transportation difficulties, and the fact that Leake Revel was the only military hospital in the area, Martin was never able to persuade the larger concert parties to visit Tor, but a number of the smaller troupes came, and if the professional actors could not spare Leake Revel a full evening of their time, they would sometimes come for half a program, and Martin would make up the rest with local talent: the Tor and New Cut Glee Club, an amateur ventriloquist from up the valley and Gladys Miller.

Gladys had a little act of her own, in which she was accompanied at the piano by Blanche, and supported (slightly) in the singing by Lily. Blanche only knew the music of a few songs, but it took her so long to learn new ones that Gladys soon gave up asking her to try. Those that Blanche did know, however, she thumped out on Lady Leake's Steinway with vigor. The soldiers thoroughly enjoyed the Miller sisters' turn because it seemed to them so like singing around the piano back home, which is exactly the way the girls thought of it too, except that they sang from an improvised stage in Lady Leake's drawing room, instead of in the bar of The Nag's Head Inn.

The Miller sisters were growing up: Gladys was now seventeen. She was a tall, cheerful girl whom no one would ever have suspected of having been a pupil of Madame Lola's. Her accent was as strong as it had ever been, her laugh just as loud, and her singing as unaffected and delightful. The only mark left upon her by the Chesterfield School of Voice was an improved ability to mimic. She still made use of the sketches that had so much amused the other students at the school. Several of them remained a part of her repertoire for the rest of her life.

When Martin first gave Gladys the opportunity to sing at Leake Revel, he put a stop to the Madame Lola technique—the smiles, nods of the head and meaningless arm gestures with which she had been taught to embellish her performances—and without these, Gladys' contributions to the soldiers' concerts were the best Tor had to offer. Blanche, who was now fifteen, did not enjoy playing at Leake Revel at all, but she felt it her duty to do as the rector asked, even though she did not altogether approve of Martin Hay —she preferred the wan intensity of the Reverend Fox. Nevertheless, she did what she could for him—teaching a Sunday school class and struggling with Gladys' piano accompaniments. Blanche was working at Dade's mill now, in the office. All day long she copied orders, and listened sympathetically to the troubles of the junior clerks.

The Miller family was impressed with Blanche's job (Blanche wore a tidy dress to work, and proper shoes, not coveralls and clogs, like Gladys) but Blanche herself was not ambitious. The only really ambitious member of the Miller household was Lily, who at the age of thirteen wanted to leave school, go on the stage, marry a lord, and have a bedroom to herself. Lily spent hours poring over the beauty pages in the women's magazines, and she would have liked very much to take lessons at the Chesterfield School of Voice, but unfortunately she had neither the money to go there nor the talent to inspire anyone to send her, even if, in the light of Gladys' experience, Holly and Fred would have permitted it.

The fourth Miller sister, Edith, was now eleven. Edith took after Blanche in appearance, but she was not efficient and capable in the way that Blanche was. Edith found everything connected with school desperately hard and puzzling, and she worried about her stupidity, even though Fred and Holly did not. "If we didn't have some people without brains," Holly told her, "how would them as has 'em be able to show theirs off?"

"You mark my words, Edie," Fred advised. "Better grow up a loving woman than wake one morning and find you've turned into a book."

"What shall I turn into, when I grow up?" Flo, the youngest sister, asked.

"The prettiest of the bunch," Fred answered at once, and his remark pleased Lily almost as much as it pleased Flo: the Millers were not envious children. Flo, at the age of nine, was the most like Holly of all Fred's daughters, which was perhaps why he spoiled her. Flo was even allowed to play with her father's rabbits, though she was apt to leave the doors open when she put the animals back in their hutches, and forget when Fred sent her out to water them.

Fred played with his younger children and confided in the elder. He would discuss business matters with Gladys and Blanche as if they were already fully grown. One night he said to Holly as he climbed into bed: "We can't be grateful enough for the lovely girls the Lord has seen fit to give to you and me."

"Well, I don't know about Lily," Holly replied. "It took her fifteen minutes to say goodnight to the Huckett boy this evening. Time enough for that, I say, when she's finished her education."

"No call for Lil to rock a cradle till she's kicked the school bucket, that it?"

"Oh *Fred!* It's lucky the girls don't have you in their act at Leake Revel. Them soldiers'd laugh so much they'd pop their stitches."

2

THE weather in Tor that September was particularly bad. It was cold all the time, and for several weeks a heavy fog lay over the valley, making it so dark that by four in the afternoon it was necessary to have the lights on indoors. Normally, Tor did not let the weather interfere with its pleasures, but this September there were a number of bad head colds going about, and several severe cases of grippe. People who did not have to go out, stayed home.

It was therefore really the weather that killed Hiram Poole. He had insisted on behaving as if everything was the same as usual. Most of each day, he sat in his usual place on the wall, waiting for the fog to lift so that he could see the Manley road and wave to anybody who happened to be going by on it. One morning (nobody knew exactly at what time) Hiram must have fainted, for he fell. He cracked his head open on the cobbled lane below the wall, and when he was found early in the afternoon (Lucy had not cooked that day, so there had been no midday meal for the family to miss him at), he was still breathing, but very near death.

Hiram did not become conscious again, which was a good thing really, for once he had had his accident, the Pooles did not want him to live. They had not had a death in the family for several years, and the moment Hiram was carried into the house, covered in mud and blood and looking as if he were dead already, they decided that the time had come to have one now. Ezra went for the doctor, but Lucy, with tears pouring in cascades down her baggy cheeks, began at once to cook for the wake feast which would start the moment Hiram's heart stopped beating. While Lucy worked, the rest of the family crowded around Hiram's bed, keening, and singing appropriate hymns:

> Lay we this dear body
> In the earth to sleep
> His sweet soul commending
> Unto Thee to keep. . . .

If by any chance Hiram had become aware of where he was, he would at once have understood that he was not expected to stay long.

The day Hiram fell was a Saturday, which, because of the war, was a full working day at Dade's mill. One of the late-shift workers brought Gladys the news, and as soon as she could (midafternoon) she went over to the Poole house, sending a message to Holly by Blanche to say where she was, and that she would be home to tea before the evening concert.

Several days before, Gladys had been told that a small concert party, on its way north from the Midlands town where it was to appear in the afternoon, would present an hour's show at Leake Revel at six tonight. The rest of the program was to be offered by local talent, including the Miller sisters.

Gladys found Hiram's little room crowded with people. She sat down on a stool at the foot of the bed. While she was there (it seemed only a short time after she had arrived), Hiram died, without making any sign.

Gladys slipped away as quickly as she could, not speaking to anyone, and leaving her raincoat behind (Mrs. John was sitting on it). Outside, Gladys was startled to find that it was fully dark. She did not know the time—neither she nor anybody in the Poole family owned a watch—but she realized that it must be late, and that she should go direct to Leake Revel.

It was raining heavily. Gladys had no hat, and her clothes were soon soaked through. As she stumbled down the lane, avoiding the larger puddles (she knew without looking for them where they lay) her mind was full of thoughts of death. They were not particularly sad thoughts. Like most country-bred children, Gladys was familiar with death. In a village so closely concerned with coal mining, death was a part of the everyday view, to be treated with respect, but not bewilderment. Every now and again, there were accidents at the Halesowen mine. The early morning whistle would blow at some hour other than the accustomed one, and the women at home in their cottages would drop whatever they were doing and hurry down the valley, not stopping to take off their aprons or (if it was winter) put on their coats. And then the dead would be brought home, and sung over and buried. It was not the suddenness of Hiram's death that shocked Gladys.

Hiram was the first man who had died while she watched him. He who had been such a great one for greetings and good-bys (beaming and waving his old hat about far more than common courtesy called for) had taken this, his most final farewell of all, without a sign of any kind to anyone. It was almost as if he hadn't wanted to interrupt the noise his family were making with their keening and wailing and their busy preparations for his wake feast. But it wasn't what Gladys had expected. She was horrified that Hiram should go like this, without a smile or a parting gesture. Surely a man's friends had a right to say good-by!

It was a longish walk from the Poole home to Leake Revel, but by a stroke of good luck Gladys was not late. She walked in at the side entrance to the house just in time to hear the clapping as the curtain fell on the first half of the show.

"Gladys!" The rector appeared suddenly out of the drawing room. He looked harassed, as he always did on concert nights. "Where have you been? In the river?"

Gladys dripped in the doorway. "I'm in time," she said. Then she stopped. She felt herself swaying. "Mr. Hay—I don't think I can—I don't think I can after all—"

Martin said: "Stay where you are. Don't move." He disappeared down the corridor. When he came back a few moments later, he was carrying a tumbler with a small quantity of brown liquid in it. "Drink that," he said. Gladys drank and coughed. "I've just heard what's happened," the rector said. "Bob Greenhaugh told me. I'm sorry. I've been expecting it." He drew Gladys away from the door.

"Now listen to me." His voice was unfamiliarly stern. "You've got to sing. I shall never forgive you if you let me down."

Gladys looked at him for a moment. "I'll be all right."

Martin took the glass from her. "Then go and find a nurse and ask her to give you some dry clothes. And do something to your hair. I'll wait for you, but I won't wait long."

Gladys hurried off, and the rector turned to find Blanche immediately behind him. Her eyes were full of tears. "When you are as old as I am," he said, and his voice had changed again, "you will know that there are times when brandy and bullying are more help than sympathy."

Gladys was gone exactly four minutes. When she stepped on the stage with her sisters, the men gave the three girls the warmest reception they had ever received. This was mostly due to Gladys' appearance. The nurse from whom she had sought help had put her into a pair of hospital pajamas (white, with a broad blue stripe) that were very much too large for her. Her feet were bare, and her hair, still very damp, hung loose to her waist.

Gladys' audience consisted of about a hundred men, most of whom had at least one bandaged limb. Because of their injuries, the men sat apart from one another without crowding; several had been wheeled in in their beds. Many wore casts, some even had casts around their bodies, and the quantity of plaster had an immobilizing effect, as if the room were full of large white parcels instead of people. If Hiram were here, Gladys thought, he'd be in the back row, waving his hat to me and behaving as if I were singing just for him. Watch your audience, that's important, Oliver Marshall had said. If I watch, she thought, I may find someone watching me who'll like me the way Hiram did.

These thoughts ran quickly through her head—they were done by the time the applause was over. Gladys, holding Lily by the hand, began her first song:

> Father, dear father, come home with me now!
> The clock in the steeple strikes one . . .

and so on, through to:

> Father, dear father, come home with me now!
> The clock in the steeple strikes three;

The house is so lonely! The hours are so long
For poor weeping mother and me.
Yes, we are alone—poor Betty is dead,
And gone with the angels of light;
And these were the very last words that she said—
"I want to kiss Papa good night."

Come home! Come home! Come home!
Please father, dear father, come home.

"And d'you know what?" Gladys added. "'E come."

They sang war songs and popular choruses, and at the end Gladys referred to her costume. "In case any of you chaps don't know it, it's wet outside. I got soaked comin' here and had to borrow these. And now—" looking down the inside of her pajama coat—"I'm finding the weather drafty. 'Oo's clothes *are* these, anyway?"

"Mine!" shouted everybody in the room.

Gladys had pretended to herself that she was singing to one man, and in a sense she was, for one member of the audience was so pleased with what he heard that when she came off the stage he was waiting to congratulate her—standing full in her way, so that she could not miss him. Joe Lansbury was the last person she expected to find at Leake Revel, and when she saw him she ran straight into his arms.

More than most businesses, concert parties and pierrot companies are subject to ups and downs. That September of 1917, the Lansbury Larks were experiencing a spell of downs. Before the outbreak of war, Joe had led a pleasant life—summers in pierrot, winters in pantomime, the in-between seasons preparing material, engaging artistes and rehearsing. Now all that was changed. Skunby-on-Sea was closed to tourists for the duration, and the theater at which Joe had made his regular pantomime appearances had been closed. He had, therefore, been driven to tour with a concert party, a job which is hard going at the best of times, but doubly so in wartime, and when one is no longer young. The troupe consisted of four artistes, Joe and Mae Lansbury, the pianist Cookie, and one other.

The fourth member of the Larks was a perpetual worry to Joe. By 1917, experienced players were extremely difficult to come by.

The able-bodied were either in the services or in munition factories, and of the remainder, those who had any real talent could command more money than Joe could afford. This left him to choose among players who drank, who were difficult to work with, or who lacked the necessary physical stamina: Joe had no patience with colleagues who tired easily, or wanted time off. During recent months, for one reason or another, the fourth member of the Lansbury Larks had changed every few weeks, a circumstance that involved Joe in extra expense, and everyone in additional rehearsal. A concert party of three is too small, although in the light of their present difficulties Joe and Mae might have considered it. But a concert party needs young blood, and that preferably female, with shapely legs (the eye of an English audience looks first at a show girl's legs). Mae's legs, in their time, had been well worth the Larks' modest price of admission, but now, although Mae was a number of years younger than her husband, nothing about her looked more youthful than it was.

So Joe ran the gamut of the available material—the dancers, the ventriloquists, the acrobats, the blowers of brass instruments, and the owners of performing animals. He took on performers who did everything except undress (undressing is a vaudeville accomplishment, not concert party), and he lost them all. His last employee had been a girl with a snake. The girl had seemed to fit into the company splendidly until the day her snake escaped and took a nap in Mae's hatbox, after which Joe was faced with the choice of keeping either the snake girl or his marriage. So when the Larks played at Leake Revel, there were only the three of them in the party. The lack of a fourth artiste was the reason why Joe felt the Larks must share the evening's bill, though this was an arrangement he very much disliked.

Like most professionals, Joe Lansbury despised amateurs, and he would never have known about Gladys Miller if it had not been for the enthusiasm she aroused in the audience. From the pantry down the hall where he was removing his make-up, Joe could hear the noise. It was so loud and prolonged that it made him curious. When he had finished changing, he went back to the drawing room to see what was going on, and there on the stage stood the long drink of water who had dogged his footsteps at Skunby-on-Sea.

Joe was very pleased. Gladys had a fine voice (he hadn't remem-

Part III

bered that) and although he could see that she had plenty to learn, he knew at once that she would do. She did not seem the kind of girl who would be afraid of hard work, she looked strong, and as if she would get along all right with Mae. What was more, thank God, she was young. She couldn't, Joe thought, be more than about eighteen.

Joe did not waste any time telling Gladys what he had in mind. Indeed, he had no time *to* waste, for the Larks had an engagement at the other end of the county the next evening—hymns and community singing, since the day would be a Sunday. Gladys, Joe told her, could have one day in which to pack, and she was to meet him on Monday at the east Yorkshire town where the Larks would be playing. He added that her pay, at least to begin with, would be very small.

When the right man appears suddenly from nowhere and proposes marriage, it may be a tremendous relief to a girl, but it can't really be a surprise: the right man is, after all, only what she has been waiting for. So Gladys, without a moment's hesitation, accepted Joe's offer. The Lansbury Larks (hadn't she always known it?) was where she belonged.

Joe had robbed parents of their young before this; it was a routine that called for a certain technique. Accordingly, after consulting an enormous pocket watch, and finding that he had an hour before he needed to leave Tor, Joe suggested that the Larks adjourn immediately to The Nag's Head, for a talk with Holly and Fred.

It was after opening time when the little party arrived at the inn (Cookie went too), and busy, as Saturday nights always were. Holly did not recognize Joe at first. She had never seen him off the stage except during Lark Walks, and on those occasions he had always worn his pierrot costume, and full make-up. He looked dowdy and down-at-heel, she thought, in his ordinary clothes—he had on a worn blue suit and brown shoes, and his hair needed redyeing: white showed through the streaky auburn. But there was no disguising Joe Lansbury's smile: it was the essential clown's smile— wide, simple, friendly and gay.

Holly had to put the Larks at a table in the kitchen. She ran back and forth with fresh hot pies for them and tankards of ale. When Joe told her why he had come, she said, *Well!* It had always seemed to her that Gladys had a lovely little voice. Mr. Hay, who produced the shows the girls put on at Leake Revel, had said some very nice things about it. But if Joe was serious, that was of course extremely kind, but the idea was out of the question. Gladys had a good steady job at Dade's mill which she enjoyed, and the Millers weren't contemplating any of their children leaving home.

Fred, standing beside his wife, did not contribute to the conversation. He knew when Holly's mind was made up. As they were shorthanded in the bar (Rose was in the army now), he excused himself as soon as he saw that Holly did not need his support, and went back to his beer pumps.

He got no help with his work. Usually on Saturdays, Gladys lent a hand, as well as Holly, but tonight he had to do everything himself. He could understand that Gladys felt the need to sit with the Larks and listen to everything they said, but it seemed quite unnecessary for Holly to do the same. The six of them, looking as thick as thieves, sat talking their heads off.

After what seemed to Fred an unconscionable time, Joe came into the bar and wrung Fred's hand. "We'll take every care of the girls, never fear," he said warmly. "They'll be treated just like members of the family." Before Fred could recover from this remark, the Larks had left.

From odd comments tossed his way by his wife and daughter during the rest of the evening, and from the excitement written large on their faces, Fred knew that Holly had changed her mind. Gladys, it seemed, was to leave home first thing on Monday morning, and Blanche was to go too.

The whole business had, Fred decided afterward, been Blanche's fault—Blanche, abetted by Mae Lansbury. Holly had taken so firm a stand to begin with against Gladys' accepting Joe's offer that Joe had decided not to press further—Gladys was, after all, a legal minor. Blanche, however, had been very much concerned. She said over and over again: "Oh Mum! Do let Gladys go! How can we tell it isn't God's will?" ("Blanche always brings God into *everything*," Holly explained crossly to Joe. "Remember the Reverend Fox? Well, that's who she caught it from.")

Then Mae weighed in. Like Holly, Mae was Derbyshire born, and although she came from a different part of the county—her mother had been linen maid at the Spa Hotel in Matlock—she did not have to have explained to her the real cause of Holly's reluctance to let Gladys join the Larks. If Joe could have taken all five of the Miller girls into his concert party, there would have been no problem: what Holly didn't like was her children being separated. Mae, however, had an idea. Would not Holly agree, she asked, that a girl should be allowed to follow her own bent in life, and do whatever most appealed to her? Indeed yes, Holly did agree. That being so, then what objection could there be to Gladys joining an old-established troupe with a fine reputation, where, Mae added reassuringly, young girls were always just as carefully chaperoned as they were at home? "Now, Mrs. Miller, there's one thing I ain't mentioned. Joe and me don't have any kids of our own and more's the pity, but if we did, the first thing I'd teach 'em 'd be that the strength of a family lies in all sticking together. I wouldn't have 'em separated from each other a minute sooner than I could help. So what would you say if we was to invite Blanche to come along too? With the two girls together, I know you wouldn't worry."

Joe said in alarm, "Steady on, Ma! With Cookie here, we've no call for another pianist, besides—"

Blanche said quickly: "If you'll take me, Mr. Lansbury, I'm ready to come. I can't help in the show, I know, but there'd be lots of other things I could do."

Gladys opened her mouth for the first time. "Don't let her, Mum! Don't let her do that!"

Holly said sharply: "If you're to be allowed to do what *you* want, Blanche can too, I suppose?" Then she turned to Joe. "I know I mustn't stand in Glad's way, Mr. Lansbury. Fred always said that. He wants the girls to settle their own lives, and that's the way I've got to feel too. But if you *could* find a place for Blanchie, I'll feel a lot better than if Glad was to go alone."

Joe was out of his depth. First of all Holly had been so uncooperative that he had about given up the whole idea, and now she seemed willing for him to take on two daughters instead of one. "We'd like to have Blanche I'm sure," he said, "but when Mae made the suggestion she was forgetting that we haven't got two salaries that we can offer."

Gladys said suddenly: "I got some money. It's back of the counter—bin there ages. Blanche can have it all and welcome, if she'll come."

And that was how it was arranged. Fred was appalled. "I don't understand you at all," he grumbled to his wife. "When we thought of sending Glad to Madame Lola's, where she'd have come home every week end, you was flat against it. And now look! The Larks may not be back this way again for *years*. And Blanche! With a good salary at Dade's and a future there, living off Glad's shoebox! What'll you think up next, I wonder?"

"Oh Fred! And I thought you'd be pleased with me for not standing in Glad's way! Blanche won't be livin' off the shoebox long. She's going to start right in on the business side where there's a lot to do, and just as soon as things pick up, she's to go on salary like Glad."

"And what's that? What is Glad's salary to be?"

Just like them, just like them! Nobody had thought to ask.

3

GLADYS and Blanche left Tor immediately after breakfast on Monday morning. The whole Miller family, as well as a large number of their friends, went along to the gibbet (the Manley bus started from the gibbet) to see them off. Holly kept a cheerful smile on her face until the bus had disappeared down the hill; then she burst into tears, and it took a glass of Guinness as well as Fred's sympathy to console her. But actually Fred was going to miss the girls more than Holly. After they went away, The Nag's Head never seemed quite the same to him again.

The girls' journey was a cross-country one; they had to change trains several times. Fortunately they each had only one small suitcase to carry. Gladys had brought the one evening dress she possessed (made to wear at the Leake Revel concerts) and Holly was to run up a second and post it as soon as it was ready.

"You know, don't you, Blanche," Gladys said, "that you are the best sister any girl ever had? When I think what you've given up—your lovely job, *and* your Sunday school class! I'll never be able to make it up to you."

"That don't signify," Blanche replied. "Any time I want I can go back to Dade's—Donaldson said so when I told him yesterday we was leavin'. As for Sunday school, they got them all over: I'll find others."

Gladys sat back and looked for a while at the gray moorland scenery. "You know how, if Mum doesn't like something," she said, "she pretends it doesn't exist?" Blanche nodded. "Well, I'd been doing the same, in a way, with the Lansbury Larks. After that talent competition, I felt sure they'd never have a job for me, so I wouldn't let myself think about them any more. And now look what's happened."

Blanche laughed. "If you're so good at telling yourself what to think," she said, "tell yourself now that you've got nothing ahead of you but hard work. Being a member of the Lansbury Larks isn't going to be a bit like going on a Lark Walk."

"I know. I'm not expecting anything."

"Yes, you are," Blanche persisted. "Bet you anything you're expecting glamour. And glamour wears off."

But in this particular instance, wise little Blanche was wrong. Long after Gladys was so familiar with the workings of concert parties, pantomimes and pierrot shows that they held neither terror nor mystery for her, the magic remained—the glamour never did wear off. To begin with, however, it was terror that predominated. At her first rehearsal with the company, it was made quite clear to Gladys as well as to the rest of the Larks that in at least one respect she was a disappointment. Joe had been so pleased with Gladys' voice and with the way in which she had handled her audience at Leake Revel that he'd forgotten, when he was in Tor, to look at her legs. Now, as she stood before the Lansburys holding her skirt high above her knees, it was obvious that Gladys' legs could only have been considered shapely by an audience of storks.

"We could pad 'em," Mae suggested.

"Paddin's no good unless there's something to pad *to*," Joe said crossly. Then he added more kindly, "All right, dear. Drop your skirt. There's nothing to be done."

Blanche said later: "Joe's face! I've seen Mum look exactly like that when the butcher's had nothing left but scrag end."

Gladys had thought that the day of her first appearance as a full-fledged Lark would be the greatest day of her life, but when it actually came about, she was far too nervous to enjoy it. "Oh Glad, *listen!"* Blanche had cried as the curtain fell. "All that applause, and some of it for you!"

"Stick a pin into me," Gladys said. "I'm numb all over."

"That's something I must remember to get—we'll be needing pins. You was wonderful."

"Did I look like I belonged?"

"Belonged!" Blanche hugged her sister. "You looked as if you'd been a Lansbury Lark all your life."

Aside from her legs, Joe was well satisfied with the rest of his choice. He found Gladys a willing recruit, almost as deeply in love with her job as he was with his, and one for whom, like him, rehearsals could never be too frequent or too long. Like him too, Gladys could eat anything and sleep anywhere—if it had not been so, the Larks' regimen would have put her in hospital. In the course of four hundred years in the business, the Lansbury family had developed a strain of human beings with the constitutions of oxen, the devotion of saints and the memories of elephants, and somehow or other Gladys managed to keep up with the standard. She had expected a gentle initiation, a little to do to begin with, more when Joe thought she was worthy. But this was not the Lansbury system. Instead, she was pitchforked straight into the full responsibilities of her job, and left to sink or swim as best she might. She was given far too much to learn, but Joe did not mind when she made mistakes or forgot her lines. All he cared about was that if she did forget, she should cover up quickly and carry on. She found it hair-raising. "Why do we always have to do everything so *fast?*" she cried to Cookie. "I scarcely get time to take a breath."

"We go fast because it's speed that makes the show," Cookie said. "That was what was wrong with you girls when we saw you in Tor. You was mighty draggy."

"But I thought an artiste was supposed to watch the audience. I don't get time to watch anything."

"You got time. You just don't have all day. You got to wind yourself up when you get in a theater, Gladdie, like you was a watch. That's the biggest difference between us and amateurs. Amateurs always play like they got all night to do it in, and all night's just about what it usually takes 'em."

Cookie was a tremendous help to her. He taught Gladys almost as much as Joe did, but in a gentler way. When he saw Gladys floundering, he did not leave her to rescue herself, but tried to help her by covering up for her at the piano. Time and again during her early weeks with the Larks, Gladys turned to Cookie for help, and always found it.

But if Joe was pleased with Gladys, of whom he had had high hopes, he was more than pleased with Blanche, of whom he had expected nothing at all. Blanche became the Larks' first full-time stage manager. Nobody told her what she was supposed to do, and she picked up the job piecemeal, as she saw the need. In next to no time she was taking care of the props, directing the locally engaged temporary staff (a couple of men to operate the lights and the curtain), prompting, hearing lines, and, being Blanche, listening to all the gossip. She also made time to help Joe with his correspondence—in concert party work, this consists almost entirely of telegrams.

It was, therefore, as much Blanche's doing as Gladys' that the fortunes of the Lansbury Larks changed for the better after the Miller sisters joined the company. Joe remembered his promise, and he put Blanche on salary as soon as he felt he could afford to (neither of the girls earned very much, but the pay was better than either they or Fred had expected). When this happened, Blanche's idea of returning to Dade's mill, which had been fading rapidly ever since she discovered how much there was for her to do for the Larks, disappeared for good. She was enjoying herself almost as much as Gladys.

As Joe had hoped she might, Gladys got along extremely well with Mae. Mae Lansbury came of a family of entertainers that reached almost as far back into history as her husband's, but whereas Joe tumbled gaily through his work, Mae made a mountain climb out of hers. It took her several hours to dress and make up, but when she was ready for the stage she was a splendid sight. She always wore low-cut gowns made of heavy material, velvet or ruched satin, and quantities of big, sparkly jewelry. With her massive, tightly corseted body poised gracefully on tiny feet, Mae did not look the ugly woman she was; she looked a queen. Nobody was left unmoved when, with a great feather fan in her long-gloved hand, Mae sang:

Call me pet names, dearest! Call me a bird
That flies to thy breast at one cherishing word;
That folds its wild wings there, ne'er dreaming of flight,
That tenderly sings there in loving delight.
Oh my sad heart is pining for one fond word.
Call me pet names, dearest! Call me a bird!

Mae's stylish dressing meant that a great deal of luggage had to accompany her everywhere, and in addition she always carried a folding screen to protect herself from drafts, and a medicine cabinet full of gargles, mouth washes, throat pastilles and concoctions of concentrated lemon. Her voice, which was a deep contralto hearty enough to hold its own on an outdoor stage against the roughest sea, was treated as if it were a tiny, delicate thing, subject to immediate disappearance. In all weathers, Mae slept with her throat tied up in a woolen scarf, and she was constantly peering, with the aid of a tongue depressor, at her stalwart tonsils.

Partly on account of her vanity but mostly on account of her luggage, Mae's idea of sharing a dressing room was to occupy at least three-quarters of the available space. The halls where the Larks played usually contained only two dressing rooms, one for women and one for men, so it was impossible for Mae to have a room to herself. Joe turned as deaf an ear as he could to the frightful rows that his wife's habits had hitherto invariably produced, but after Gladys joined the Larks there was peace. Even Mae was surprised when the new member of the troupe, slapping on her make-up in a shadowy corner under a single naked light bulb, made no comment. "That Gladys is a real find," she confided to her husband. "I don't know when we've had a lovelier girl."

4

That fall, the Larks traveled all over the North and North Midlands of England, with an occasional trip into Wales. Sometimes they stayed in a town for as much as three days, but mostly they stopped one night. All their journeys were made by train. As much as schedules could be planned, long journeys were made on Sun-

Part III

days, and the few trains that ran on Sundays stopped at every station. The Larks, fortified by Blanche's sandwiches and a supply of beer, spread themselves comfortably over the railway carriage and passed the time dozing, gossiping, and (as if they did not get enough already) singing songs.

It was a good life: every member of the Larks was completely absorbed in the Larks, to the exclusion of all else. However late the troupe arrived in a town, and however tired they might be, they always went first to the hall or theater where they were to play. The local manager would be there to greet them, and the Larks did not turn to thoughts of supper and bed until they had examined every detail of their accommodation to their satisfaction, or at least until they were fully acquainted with the worst.

Mae's first thought on arrival in a town was her dressing room. As often as not, the broken window she had complained about last year would not have been repaired, and the light that didn't work last time still didn't work now. Once, in a cotton town in Lancashire that the Larks had not visited before, Mae discovered that the ladies of the company were expected to dress in a corridor only separated from the audience by a pair of swing doors.

"I'll get a padlock, then we'll be all right," Blanche said, hurrying off after the manager.

"No place to fit a padlock," the manager told her. "But I tell you what we can do. Archie!" Archie was the assistant. "You got any privates?"

As might have been expected, Archie had. He produced a large white card with PRIVATE printed on it, and when this had been nailed to the audience's side of the swing doors, Mae was mollified.

Concert party artistes are expected to do a little of everything—sing, dance, act and contribute some "speciality" of their own to the program. Gladys sang, danced a little and presented her Madame Lola sketch, and she also took part in three or four very short plays. This was not as hard work as it sounds, for her parts were extremely small, and the plays were little more than incidents, in which the point could be seen coming some time before it arrived. One such, a very popular item, opened with Cookie seated at a table covered with books and papers, on the side of which hung a sign reading REGISTRAR OF MARRIAGES.

Enter Gladys.

GLADYS. You rang, sir?

COOKIE. Yes, Miss Miller, I did. Is there any sign of that man Lansbury yet?

GLADYS. No sir, absolutely none.

COOKIE. Very odd. In all my years' experience as a registrar of marriages I have never known anything like it. He comes here in the ordinary way, makes all the arrangements to be married on Monday morning, and doesn't turn up. Now it's Friday, and not a word of explanation of any kind.

GLADYS. Perhaps the lady changed her mind in time, sir.

COOKIE. Miss Miller, that is not the proper attitude to take to your work. No, the matter is a serious one and I can only think that Mr. Lansbury suffered some accident which has prevented . . . (*The door opens and in comes* JOE, *dressed very loudly as a bridegroom.*) Good Heavens! Here is the very man we're speaking about. Well, Mr. Lansbury?

JOE. Good morning, good morning! I've come to be married.

COOKIE. Are you aware that you are four days late?

JOE. Yes, but I couldn't help it. I got all ready to come on Monday, and I was called away on a job. I had to go and see to it, it was urgent.

COOKIE. And where, may I ask, is the other contracting party?

JOE. The what?

COOKIE. Where is the lady you wish to marry?

JOE. Ellen!!! 'Strewth! I've forgotten to bring her! I'll have to go back.

He makes for the door.

COOKIE (sternly). My good man—are you a drunkard?

JOE. No, no, certainly not. I'm a *plumber!*

Black out.

Singing was the mainstay of the program, old songs as well as the current popular war songs: "Keep the Home Fires Burning," "Tipperary," "Pack Up Your Troubles," "The Yanks Are Coming." Gladys always had at least one solo number. In one of these, she appeared on the stage with a little girl's pinafore tied over her dress, and a big black bow on the top of her head. Waving an enormous cardboard beer tankard at the audience, she sang:

Part III

> Pure water is the best of drinks
> That man to man can bring
> But who am I that I should have
> The best of everything?
> Let princes revel at the pump,
> Let peers with ponds make free,
> For whiskey, wine, or even beer,
> Is good enough for me.

Not many weeks after Gladys joined the Larks, she caught a cold which reduced her voice to a croak. Joe sent Blanche for the doctor, Cookie prepared hot poultices, and Mae offered Gladys the full hospitality of the traveling medicine chest. Nothing did any good. Gladys suggested to Joe that a croak might add to her song rather than detract from it, but Joe, who had been trained by Mae into thinking that a singer must have a voice if she is going to sing, was unconvinced. Concert parties never have understudies (if you can stand up, you go on) so there was no question that Gladys' affliction would prevent her from appearing, and in the end Joe had no choice but to let her have her way. Gladys bought herself a large mourning handkerchief—white, with a wide black border—and when the time came for her beer song, she explained to the audience that she had recently been orphaned and could not sing properly for grief. The song went down so well that, whether Gladys had a cold or not, the croak and the mourning handkerchief became part of the act. What a girl, thought Joe, what a girl! Whoever heard of a female singer who was even more successful when she lost her voice?

The Larks operated on a percentage basis; that is to say, sixty per cent of the gross takings were theirs, the owner of the hall in which they played taking the remainder. Sometimes Joe would receive a guaranteed sum, but mostly he depended, as his traveling-player ancestors had done, on what the mood of the public brought him in. When the Larks were in steady work they did well, but even during their weeks out, things were better for Joe after the Miller girls joined the company. The Millers never grumbled if there was a lack of work; unexpected holidays delighted them. The longest of these occurred at Christmastime, when Joe closed the show for a month in order to fulfill a pantomime engagement in a small town in the Potteries. While he worked, Mae stayed home (Gladys was astonished to discover that the Lansburys did have a home— they owned a bungalow at Skunby-on-Sea) and the Miller girls returned to Tor. Because he had no job at the moment and nowhere particular to go, Cookie accompanied them.

5

THERE was snow in Tor on Christmas Eve. It fell slowly, in large flakes, and when it had blanketed the moor and the valley, it made the village seem even more isolated than it normally was. The children brought their sleds out and there was skating on the Thorne. Water pipes froze, and the army produced a number of small portable oil stoves to warm the unheated rooms at Leake Revel. Most of the Christmas festivities this year centered on the convalescent home. There was a tree, and presents for the men, a concert and a huge Christmas dinner. For the first time in Tor's history *The Messiah*, which was always presented in Tor Church on Christmas Day afternoon, was sung twice. The Tor and New Cut Glee Club and the augmented church choir assembled again on Boxing Day afternoon, to sing in the Leake Revel drawing room. Gladys sang the soprano solos, and a place was made for Cookie among the baritones so that he should not feel left out.

Cookie had quickly become a close friend of both Blanche and Gladys. They had been prepared to treat him with the respect they owed a player of such long standing, but Cookie would have none of it. Over countless cups of tea, he confided in Blanche, telling her that he was an old man (Cookie was thirty) and, with cockney cheerfulness, about his unsuccessful love affairs and his chronic indigestion. "Isn't it terrible, Glad!" Blanche's talent as a confidante did not include the ability to keep confidences to herself. "Cookie is always falling in love, but no girl ever wants him permanent."

"Perhaps he has a secret vice," Gladys suggested.

"Well, if he has," Blanche said practically, "I hope it's drink. Our beer's the kind he likes the best."

Cookie had been born within the sound of Bow Bells, and even a broken heart, or a succession of them, did not depress him for

Part III 125

long. "Being turned down by women ain't what you'd call enjoyable," he explained to Blanche, "but after the first fifty years you get used to it, I'm told."

Cookie was touched by the affection offered him by the Millers. ("Mr. Cook an orphan!" Holly said to her husband the first evening. "Can't picture it at all, can you?") Holly and Blanche mothered him, Fred treated him enough like a member of the family to put him to work (he was not quick enough to serve behind the counter, so he played the bar piano for the clientele to sing), Edith and Flo played games with him—he taught them London games, unknown in Derbyshire—and Lily listened open-mouthed to his advice on acting. She was determined to join the Lansbury Larks the moment she was old enough to do so.

Lily charmed Cookie because she was so like Gladys to look at, and it was Gladys that, somewhat to his annoyance, Cookie cared for. The situation puzzled him, for Gladys was not petite and clinging and blonde like most of Cookie's girls, and she was far too young. It had never been his habit to lose his heart to anyone thirteen years younger than himself. Cookie had, however, the sense to keep his feelings to himself. Only Fred suspected them. "Cookie sweet on our Glad, d'you suppose?" he asked Holly.

Holly reassured him at once. "Oh no, Fred. He's much too old."

Cookie was taken sledding and skating and on bus rides—the Millers liked to ride on top at the front, beside the notice which read DRIVER BELOW—DO NOT STAMP FEET. In return, he entertained them with stories. Like all actors, Cookie loved an appreciative audience, and the Millers could not have been improved upon in that respect. "They was all men in the Larks the summer the war started," he told them one evening. "There were seven of us. We used to go all over, giving shows at army camps, and one we went to (it was outside Sheffield) was a real camp too—all tents. When we got there we found that the tent we was to dress in had nothing in it but the pole that held its middle up—no table, no chairs, no nothing. So I go for the sergeant who's supposed to be looking after us, see, and who d'you think I run into? Alec, the dancer fellow who was with us at Skunby in 1913—remember him?"

The Millers nodded.

"Well," Cookie went on, "Alec says not to bother the sergeant, he'll see to everything for us. So we go and get a cuppa tea at the canteen, and by the time we done that, Alec has everything fixed. And is it! Trust the army. We got seven chairs, seven mirrors, seven hand basins, with a jug of water in each, and seven bits of soap; seven pieces of essential furniture, and beside them seven toilet rolls. . . ."

It interested Cookie to notice the way in which the Miller family treated The Nag's Head and Tor Church as if both were different pieces of the same home. One chatted and laughed in either place, though not while Fred was checking the till or counting the wine, nor while the choir sang or Martin prayed. Walking home on Christmas Day after *The Messiah* to high tea at the inn, Cookie said to Gladys: "You're lucky having Tor to come home to. It's a place that'll never change."

Tor might not change, but already Gladys had. Even Lady Leake noticed it. She said to the rector: "Your protégée's voice is better than ever, in spite of those terrible lessons she took in Chesterfield, and whatever it is she is up to now. There's a kind of glow about her when she's singing—that's new."

"But not surprising," Martin said. "She's in the job she always wanted to be in."

"So is my daughter Catherine, but I don't notice a similar improvement in *her* skin."

Fred Miller had noticed the same thing, though he didn't express it in the same way. "You sang fine, real fine this afternoon—I couldn't take my eyes off ye," he said to his daughter. "And if that ain't praise from your old Dad, I don't know what is."

Gladys hugged him. Fred added: "What's it like—the big world you're livin' in now?"

Gladys laughed. "You should see it, Dad—we don't! We're so busy working or sleeping or traveling, the only time we even know where we are is when we see a name on a railway station."

"That's right, Mr. Miller," Cookie said. "Where we live when we're with the Larks is a lot smaller a place than Tor is. We don't get to meet folks much—any time we have off is when they're working."

Late on Christmas night, Gladys said to her father, "Dad, do they ever let brides sing at their own weddings?"

Fred scratched his head. "Can't say as I can recall any as did."

He looked at her thoughtfully, "D'you have any particular man in mind?"

"No, but it was so lovely singing in the old church this afternoon, it reminded me of Margaret Leake, and I wondered."

6

IN MOST of the towns where the Lansbury Larks played, there were rooming houses that specialized in catering to theatricals. Joe and Mae knew them all. They offered two types of living accommodation—in one, meals were supplied, and in the other, the guest did his own shopping and his landlady cooked and served him his purchases. Theatrical landladies, even the best of them, are not inventive. The Larks' meals consisted of breakfast, midday dinner, high tea and a bedtime snack, and the menus leaned heavily in the direction of starches; salads and fresh fruit were neither supplied nor expected. Tea accompanied all meals, a large pot, black and strong. Guests provided their own beer. Joe and Mae Lansbury preferred the former system of living, for Mae was a forgetful and unimaginative housekeeper. Mae told the girls that they could decide for themselves later on how they would live, but for the present they were to stay in the same rooming house as Joe and herself, and eat with them. Mae was a kindly but firm chaperone. The girls were not allowed to refuse food, however unattractive it might be, nor leave any. "You got to keep your strength up in this business," Mae told them. "Joe and me ain't got no patience with thin girls, or girls that's picky feeders."

"I can't help being thin," Gladys objected.

"You'll improve," Mae assured her. "There's no finer bosom-builder in the world than singing."

Mae made no rules about the hours the girls kept—she knew there was no need. After a day of rehearsing, performing, packing or traveling, Gladys and Blanche were only too ready to fall into bed. One night Gladys said to her sister, "Mae's not at all strict, is she? We could go out dancing any night."

"We could if we had the feet," Blanche replied.

The most alarming part about a Larks' show, Gladys thought, was the way Joe wouldn't always stick to the script. He loved to head off on his own. Sometimes he would talk to the audience about her: "You see this lassie here? She comes from Tor, and I'll let you into a secret. The only reason she's here at all is that she's out to catch *him*—" indicating Cookie. "Make a fine pair, won't they?" Cookie was five feet four. "But 'e don't mind. 'E's thinkin' of 'is comfort. Married to her, 'e'll always know what the weather's like upstairs."

Cookie advised: "Don't take any notice. Just let Joe blether on. He'll get back to the script when he's ready for it. But if he speaks to you, mind you answer him. It don't matter what you say, as long as you say something."

There was a great deal to learn, even a language. "Nobody scarpers the letty around here, I'll be bound!" Joe exclaimed admiringly one day, referring to the agility of the Larks' present landlady in seeing that nobody left her house without paying his rent. Gladys and Blanche soon absorbed "skip" for a clothes basket, and "tabs" for the curtains, but when Cookie said to them, "Hurry, the ghost's walking!" he had to explain that he meant this was pay day.

There were also points of etiquette to be mastered. Blanche was instructed that she must give the landlady free tickets for the show, a gesture that usually encouraged the landlady to make up a party, so that the two free seats became half a dozen sold. Gladys also had to have a photograph of herself taken, for insertion in the frame which the Larks carried around with them, and hung outside the hall where they played. The pictures in this frame were appropriately graded in size: large photographs of Joe and Mae, a smaller one of Cookie and a smaller one still of Glad.

Rank was not only observed within the Larks' photograph frame. Gladys only spoke to Joe if he spoke to her first. But he was not at all unfriendly. Although stern and critical in rehearsals, he would often go out of his way to help her. One night the Larks were playing in a suburb of Manchester, in a small hall in a poor part of the city. It was raining hard, every seat was taken, and there were people standing—as many as were allowed. The Larks had assembled on the little stage and were waiting for the curtain to go up. Joe said to Gladys: "Notice the smell? Grease paint and dust on this side,

Part III

wet clothes, cheap tobacco and people, on that. There's nothing quite like it in the world, and every time I smell it, it scares me to death."

"*Scares* you?"

Joe nodded. He took Gladys' hand and led her to a peephole in the curtain. "Take a look and you'll see what I mean."

The auditorium was less brightly lighted than the stage, and Gladys could not see anything clearly. There was a smoky haze, and white faces in the foreground.

"Those folk haven't spent the day on the beach," Joe said. "They've been to work, and they're tired as well as wet. Most of 'em don't have much money, by the looks, and yet they've all paid out to come and watch you and me. If that don't scare you, you're in the wrong job."

On another occasion when the Larks were assembling on the stage before the curtain rose on their opening number, Joe pointed in the direction of the audience and said to Gladys: "There's a block of ice between us and them. It's at every performance, and you never can tell ahead of time how thick it is, or how long it's going to take you to melt it."

But most of the time, Joe treated Gladys as if she were one of the company props—a piece of the furniture. One evening, she was standing just inside the door of the women's dressing room, tying her shoes. She had nothing on except the shoes, a pair of stockings and a long, full skirt. Joe knocked sharply at the door and came in over his knock to speak to Mae. As he passed Gladys, he ran his fingers lightly down her bare spine. "Nice clean back," he said approvingly. "Could eat me dinner off it."

7

At Easter, the Larks finished their tour. Joe disbanded the company and retired to Skunby-on-Sea to plan his summer pierrot program.

It is customary for English pierrot shows to open for the season on Whitmonday, which is a public holiday. In 1918, Easter fell early, which meant that Whitsunday fell early too—on the nineteenth of May. Pierrots do not like an early Whitsun because although it gives them a longer summer, the weather at the seaside in May is apt to be chilly and to keep holiday-makers at home. This year, however, the early Whitsun was no disadvantage so far as the Larks were concerned. The beach and pier at Skunby-on-Sea were still closed on account of the war, but Joe had obtained a contract with the city of Derby to provide a twice-daily pierrot show in the Arboretum, one of their public parks.

Playing a city park is an attractive proposition to a pierrot company. Some English city parks have beautiful little open-air theaters, and a steady income is assured, for the pierrots are paid out of the taxes—an inclusive rate for the job. The pierrots have to give their performances whether it rains or not and, although being funny in a downpour is hardly a congenial occupation, the show always had a good audience. At Derby, seats were fourpence, but anyone could stand on the grass at the back for nothing, and there were always taxpayers willing to watch from under open umbrellas rather than miss what was going on.

Joe Lansbury, for the first time in his life, knew in April where he was likely to stand financially the following September. He ordered new pierrot costumes for everybody (two outfits apiece) and had Cookie's piano repainted and renovated. It was Joe's custom to engage a different supporting cast each season—he and Mae felt that this was essential when so much of their program material was the same, or nearly the same, every year—but the Larks had never played the Derby Arboretum before, and so this time Joe decided to keep the cast he had, and increase the number of artistes to six, the size he best liked the Lansbury Larks to be.

The company rehearsed for three weeks at Skunby-on-Sea before they opened in Derby. Sometimes rehearsals took place in the living room of the Lansburys' bungalow, and sometimes in a dance hall in the town that had been closed for the duration of the war. While the Larks were at Skunby, Gladys and Blanche lived with the Pegler family at The Dunes. Mrs. Pegler was delighted to see them again. "My, my! Don't you look the actress!" she exclaimed approvingly, when Gladys pirouetted in front of her in her new costume of white cotton, with its black pompons and little black cap. "Remember how you used to carry on about the pierrots in the old days? Time and again I said to Pegler, 'Depend upon it, that child's going to grow up into *something*.'"

The new members of the Lansbury Larks were Bubbles King, a soubrette—all soubrettes, Gladys was to learn, were called Bubbles or Billie or Bobbie—and a light comedian, Benny Buckell, who, among other things, acted as feed, or straight man, for Joe. Bubbles King was twenty-seven. She had golden blond hair and magnificent legs (Joe was not making *that* mistake again). Bubbles had been in show business all her life; she was competent, garrulous and quarrelsome. Bubbles' world was full of people who, she claimed, insulted her, discriminated against her and tried to take advantage of her—a combination of circumstances that made her a mine of gossip and scandal. The Millers had never met anyone like Bubbles King before. They had never met anyone like Benny Buckell either. Benny was tall and slight (Gladys guessed him to be five years younger than Cookie—he was actually three years older), and he had blue eyes, thin, sandy hair, and a small, neatly trimmed mustache that covered the lower half of his lip. A violin case and a folding trouser press traveled with Benny everywhere he went, and in Gladys' opinion, formed after being in his company for ten minutes, he was a man of incomparable good looks and brilliance.

Neither Bubbles nor Benny took more than the barest notice of the Miller sisters, but they took a considerable amount of notice of each other. Bubbles laughed uproariously at Benny's jokes, and they usually arrived together at the Lansbury bungalow for rehearsals, and left together afterward. "Do you suppose they're secretly married?" Gladys said to Blanche.

"No," Blanche replied. "They don't act like married people. They fidget too much."

On the Larks' last night in Skunby, Benny invited the whole troupe to drink with him at The Tired Man. He sat at the bar with one arm around Bubbles' waist and bought beer for everybody except Gladys. She was given Bristol Cream. This was, he explained, in order that she might toast her pierrot costume, now packed in all its pristine freshness in a skip at Skunby railway station. "A first pierrot costume," Benny said, "is a great occasion. Congratulations and all the luck in the world, Gladys Miller." The others applauded, and Benny leaned forward and gently kissed her.

Afterward, when Cookie was seeing the girls home to The Dunes, Blanche said: "They're a rum two, if you ask me."

"Who are?"

"Benny Buckell and Bubbles King."

"Oh, Benny's all right," Cookie answered. "He's had a difficult time, though, being Buck Buckell's son."

"Who is Buck Buckell?"

Cookie sighed. "The ignorance of you two girls," he said, "at times has me beat. In the first place, the question is who *was* Buck Buckell—he's dead. Buck Buckell was one of the best light comedians, if not *the* best, that England ever had. You should have heard Buck singing 'Lardy-dah!'—nothing like it. Well, Benny is Buck's son. Most sons want to be something different from their fathers. Benny wants to be the same. But he never will—he ain't got Buck's talent. Benny's a good feed, but he don't rate more than that."

"In *my* opinion—" Gladys began hotly, but Blanche interrupted her.

"And Bubbles? What about her?"

"Bubbles—" Cookie hesitated. "Bubbles is all right too. Easy, but all right."

"Is being easy like being a good feed?"

"Well yes, in a way, quite like," Cookie said.

8

FRED and Holly Miller and their three younger daughters came over from Tor for the Lansbury Larks' opening performance at the Derby Arboretum on Whitmonday evening. The weather was perfect. Fred bought everybody a "program." This gave no indication of the acts to be presented, but it gave Gladys a thrill. It read:

The Lansbury Larks Are Here!
You Can't Go to Skunby-on-Sea This Year, but Never Mind!
Skunby-on-Sea Has Come to You.
Daily at 6 P.M. Wet or Fine.
All Seats Fourpence. Children Half Price.

Come and Spend an Evening with Your Friends Old and New:
    Joe Lansbury (You All Know Me!)
    Mae Lansbury (The Queen of Song)
    Benny Buckell (Romance and a Violin)
    Bubbles King (A Curl and a Twirl)
    Gladys Miller (The Larks' Own Nightingale)
    John Cook (Piano Wizard)
        Programs Changed Twice Weekly.
Make the Lansbury Larks *Your* Summer Habit!

Joe set the narrow little stage just the way he set his stage at Skunby, with Cookie's piano at one side and five white stools for the other artistes in a semicircle against the backdrop. The show opened with the Larks, in their starched new pierrot costumes, lined up along the footlights singing together:

> The Lansbury Larks
> In Derby's parks,
> For fun you cannot beat 'em,
> For dance and song
> All summer long,
> Come to the Arboretum!

Then the pierrettes, each kneeling on one knee, thrummed ukuleles. Ukulele playing was a trial to Gladys—she disliked both the feel and the sound of the instrument and she never learned to play it well. Next, Joe told stories, several of them based on the perennial rivalry between Derbyshire and the adjoining county of Nottingham: "I went into a butcher's shop in town the other day, on King Street I think it was, and asked for a sheep's head. You ever have sheep's head at your house? Mighty good eating, sheep's head. Well, the butcher he has one, and I say, 'Is this 'ere Nottingham meat?' Butcher says, 'No, this animal's from Derbyshire.' 'Then it won't do,' I says. 'The Missus she comes from Nottingham, and she says to get Nottingham meat.' 'Won't take a minute to put that right sir,' says the butcher (very polite, calling me sir), 'You just wait a minute while I take its brains out.'"

Bubbles danced, Benny, one lock of hair falling forward over his eyes, played the violin, and there were sketches and popular wartime choruses in which the audience joined, such as "Sister Susie's Sewing Shirts for Soldiers."

As usual, the Larks changed to evening dress during the intermission. All of them were given a splendid reception, but the favorite of the evening was Gladys Miller. Joe had given her serious songs, but she was even more successful with humorous ones:

> If you please you see I'm a domestic,
> Or what some would call "servant gal,"
> My missus she calls me Sarah,
> But father for short calls me Sal,
> I'm general slave round the corner,
> My wages is small, you'll agree,
> I'm slaving from morn until midnight,
> And I finds my own sugar and tea—

But if I only sit down for a minute to catch me breath—

> The bell goes a-ringing for Sarah,
> Sarah, Sarah,
> The bell goes a-ringing for Sarah,
> From morning until night. . . .

Gladys performed this number—it had several long verses—with such gaiety and pathos that the audience, Joe knew, would be coming back again and again throughout the summer for more. Joe was not surprised. Gladys had been improving steadily since her first appearance with the Larks. He was very proud of her. "How does it feel, havin' 'em clappin' for you?" he asked her.

"Like ale on a real hot day!" Gladys replied.

After the show, the Larks, as was their custom, came down from the stage and mixed with the audience. Benny was kept very busy during this part of the program. While the men gossiped and joked with Joe, and friends from Tor flocked around Gladys, wives and daughters lined up in front of Benny, asking for his autograph.

"Quite a peach, Miss King," Fred whispered to his wife. "We'll 'ave to put Rose into stockings with 'oles all over 'em when we get her back from the army."

"Mr. Buckell's my fancy," Holly said. "Ever so much the gent, isn't he?"

"Glad thinks so," Blanche commented. "Every time he's on, she—"

"What did you think of the show as a whole, Dad?" Gladys interrupted.

"Well, love," Fred replied, "the reason I come was to take a look at you, and you was well worth the journey."

9

THE Lansbury Larks company that summer was one of Joe's best. The audiences were, on the whole, more sedate than the Larks' audiences at Skunby, partly because the people were not away from home, and partly because it was now the fifth summer of the war. Derbyshire folk looked more dowdy than they had before good cloth became scarce, but they were more prosperous. Every Larks' audience contained a large number of men in uniform, and for their benefit Joe put Bubbles into the program more often and Mae less. Otherwise the Larks' show was essentially the same in content as a seaside pierrot program.

The Arboretum theater was a simple structure. It consisted of a shell-pattern bandstand, in front of which, on a roped-off area of a lawn, were set about three hundred wooden folding chairs. Beyond the lawn was a footpath, across which another lawn, with a small white sign on it, PRAMS NOT ALLOWED BEYOND THIS POINT, sloped upward. On fine evenings, the Larks were apt to have audiences on both lawns, though the people on the farther one were too far away to hear. Back of the bandstand were three tents, two for dressing rooms and a third for props.

Gladys was teamed with five professionals now, only one of whom (Cookie) was on the lookout to help her. The challenge was a strenuous one. She had to dance, play the ukulele, act, sing and—most difficult of all—be in the right place at the right time and look as if she belonged there. But she was learning fast. The speed of the show troubled her much less than it had at first, and if she made a mistake she was not embarrassed—the pierrots did not seem to mind correcting her in the full hearing of the audience:

JOE: "I went in swimming, and I caught a cold."

GLADYS: "You caught a cold?"
JOE: "No—swimming is the point."
GLADYS: "Oh! You went in *swimming?*"

She loved every minute of it. One morning, Blanche said: "What d'you think I saw in Market Street today? Roses!"

"Since I bin a Lark," Gladys said solemnly, "every day's been like a whole bouquet of 'em."

From Bubbles, she learned how to fix her hair so that however much she threw herself about on the stage, it stayed neatly in place. Bubbles also taught her how to care for the fragile fishnet stockings that are part of a pierrette's costume, and make one pair last several months. (*"They* ought to supply them," Bubbles grumbled, "shoes as well as stockings, but they never do. No management has the decency, as you'll soon find out. I've known girls work in stockings with darns showin' and even holes. I got too much pride for that, and pride's expensive in this business.")

From Benny, Gladys learned nothing but stage fright. While she was perfectly happy to work alongside such seasoned troupers as Joe and Mae, when it came to sharing the dialogue with Benny, she was filled with terror. In the sketches and songs they had together, her knees knocked as they had never knocked before. The thought that he, as well as everybody else, might notice this appalled her. But apparently no one did.

Benny was handsome, and he had the kind of charm that for years had been bowling over women far more sophisticated than little Gladys Miller of The Nag's Head Inn. So it was not surprising that she should have toppled in his path like a ninepin. No stage of her development, least of all falling in love, came to her gently and easily.

During the season, Joe allowed Gladys to put a version of her Madame Lola sketch into the program. It concerned an elocution lesson ("Aa, Ee, Aya, Awe, Ewe . . . Hay, He, Hi, Ho, Hugh. . . . If you want to talk like a nob, do as the nobs do. Before you speak, take a bite out of an unripe quince. . . .")

Gladys was very happy, as she had every right to be, about her work. She was not at all happy about Benny Buckell. She was miserable when she was not with him, and even more miserable when she was. After that one brief kiss over a wine glass at The Tired Man, Benny had returned to normal, never speaking to her except (very occasionally) about her work. Blanche, when apprised of her sister's tight heartstrings and hollow stomach, said: "Couldn't you possibly make it Cookie, Glad? Cookie so badly needs someone to love him."

"Perhaps Benny—" Gladys suggested.

"Oh, dear me, no! Look at the way the women flock around him."

"I know, I know."

"He's got skirts pursuin' him all day long."

Benny had, but it was not only skirts: middle age was after him too. As Cookie had said, things weren't easy for him: to live up to a father is much harder than to live one down. Benny's life had been strewn with first-class opportunities—he did not know what it was to be refused admission to a producer's office. Many producers were family friends, glad not only to see Benny, but also to take him to lunch. And Benny could always get auditions. What he couldn't get was the work. Almost everybody had been fond of Buck Buckell, and all were well disposed toward his son, but they were not well enough disposed to risk their money or their reputations.

It took Benny until he was thirty-three to appreciate this, and to realize that ambition is no substitute for talent and middle age no respecter of either. The reason why he was with the Lansbury Larks this summer instead of rehearsing in London for George Garrison's new all-star revue was that Joe Lansbury thought him worth employing, and George Garrison did not. And time, time to prove to George Garrison that he was mistaken, was running out, taking with it, for the first time in Benny Buckell's life, a large part of his self-confidence and hope.

In spite of the impression to the contrary that he had given Gladys Miller, Benny had noticed her. How could he help it? For one thing, she was always in his way. She was the first person he saw when he arrived at the Arboretum and the last person he saw when he left. So far as he could make out, she lived on the stepladder that reached from the park to the little stage. Benny had had admiring novices dog his path before this, but not novices who possessed the one thing that had made Buck different from the others—quality on the stage. Gladys was raw still, and George Garrison, if he saw her now, might have no use for her at all. But later, in five years, or maybe less? Benny was certainly not unaware of Gladys Miller. She interested him very much.

They had spent most of the summer at the Arboretum before it occurred to Benny that in Gladys might lie a solution to his own problem. She had the talent, he the knowledge—the answer was for them to work as a team. The idea germinated slowly, for Benny had domestic troubles on his hands. Unfortunately, he had grown tired of Bubbles King before she had grown tired of him, a circumstance that caused his involvement in a succession of frightful scenes, all of which wore him to a rag, as Bubbles intended that they should. Bubbles, who bloomed under the stimulation of rows, was at the same time enjoying a long-drawn-out battle with Mae, on the hardy old topic of dressing room space. In this fight, Bubbles had right on her side, which would probably have made a difference if the protagonist had been anyone else but Mae Lansbury. Mae took no notice of anything Bubbles said until she became abusive. Then the fur flew. Mae possessed a seemingly endless fund of invective, so colorful that even Bubbles was reduced to tears by it, and the Miller sisters, standing by in fascination, had their vocabularies as well as their knowledge of life abruptly enlarged.

The City Parks Department allowed Joe Lansbury all the help he needed behind the scenes, and this meant that Blanche had time to go to church almost as often as she wanted to. Her religious devotion was as avid as ever—she sang hymns all day long. The temporary help soon grew used to sorting props to the strains of:

> With thy sheep, Lord, deign to mate me,
> From the he-goats separate me.

Blanche also found time to befriend the city's stage-struck young. Throughout the summer, large numbers of these found their way to the prop tent behind the stage. They wanted jobs, any jobs, but all they got was Blanche's sympathy and large cups (without saucers) of strong, sweet tea, for Joe had given it out as his unbreakable rule that only experienced actors and actresses were invited to join the Lansbury Larks.

This was not true (unless one allowed that the Miller sisters' act in the Leake Revel soldier shows constituted previous professional experience), for in August, during the week following her fourteenth birthday, Joe took on Lily Miller. This was a mistake on his part, but an understandable one. After what had happened to the fortunes of the Lansbury Larks already, Joe felt that any Miller sister was welcome in the company. Lily was just as keen and hardworking as Gladys was, but unfortunately she had no voice to speak of, little acting ability, and legs like those of an underfed filly. Joe only permitted her to appear in the second half of the program and he paid her exactly half the salary he had started Gladys at. Lily was delighted. She had one song-and-dance number with the rest of the company, and a part in a playlet that concerned the mistaken identity of twins. Lily and Gladys were nowhere near alike enough to make this idea seem plausible, but they were better casting than many of the girls who had appeared in the sketch since Joe's grandfather had first introduced it.

Lily's arrival in the company had, however, one very satisfactory result. Mae and Bubbles both wanted to mother her, and this effected an armistice, though not peace, between them. The ladies felt it undignified to shout and swear in front of a child, and so they reverted to an extreme politeness, coupled with the frequent exchange of the kind of smiles little Lily could have skated on.

Meanwhile, Benny Buckell watched Gladys' work. He was well aware that their success as a team would depend on her. For Benny to consider devoting the rest of his life to the support of another artiste was a complete change of focus for him: sharing the limelight had never been among his ambitions. It was a gamble, but the chances of success seemed good. It occurred to him that they might present an act comprising songs with violin accompaniment, a violin solo and a patter sketch in which Gladys would play the leading role and he would feed. Benny was deliberately placing himself in the background, though still in evidence.

Benny noticed that what audiences liked best about Gladys was not her lovely serious voice, nor her scratchy humorous one, nor even her ability to mimic; it was simply that she made them feel that she was one of themselves. People would laugh just to see how happy she looked up there before she even opened her mouth at all, for already to Gladys, the miner and his family, the soldier and his girl, the giggling shop assistants and the raucous children who swarmed into the Arboretum on matinee days, were not just members of audiences, they were her family. Joe had some of this feeling for them too and so had Cookie, but Bubbles, Benny and Mae had none, which was probably why Joe played the children's matinees with a cast of four rather than seven.

The children's matinees, unlike the other shows, were not rehearsed in detail. What the Lansbury Larks provided was more a game than a performance—play proceeded according to the fancy of the players, those on the stage as well as off it.

Benny attended every children's matinee that August. He sat in the back row, over to one side, under the trees, and he thought Gladys' performances magnificent. She held the children's attention from start to finish, ordering them about and bullying them, and they loved it. "Now come on—everybody's to sing. If I see anybody not singing, I'll call the police."

There was a man named Dunderbeck invented a machine,
It was for grinding sausage meats and it did go by steam,
Those kitten cats and long-tailed rats no more they will be seen,
They're all ground up in sausage meats by Dunderbeck's machine.

One afternoon, Gladys noticed that all the children were laughing at her except one little boy. She stopped the show and pointed at him. "What's the matter with you?" she demanded. "Ain't I funny enough for you?"

The little boy stared. He was about seven years old. His mother, a pale young woman, answered for him. "If you please, miss, Robin don't hear none."

Gladys turned to the rest of the audience. "What shall we do? We got to make Robin laugh."

"Try standing on your head, miss," someone suggested.

So Gladys tried. Calling Lily over to help her, she threw herself about the stage in such absurd antics that she soon had the little deaf boy laughing.

Benny did not approach Gladys with his project until he had ready both a program for her to consider, and a job. Joe Lansbury was to go on tour again as soon as his summer season at the Arboretum finished, but since he would employ a fresh company, the Larks, with the exception of Mae and Cookie, would be out of a job once the Derby contract was completed. Joe, however, had a large number of relatives in the business, and it was the habit of the Lansbury family to pass around among each other such artistes as had proved their worth. Joe's brother, Arthur Lansbury, whose wife hailed from Edwinstowe on the edge of Sherwood Forest, ran a company called the Merry Men. Arthur had already been to Derby and seen the Larks, and Benny had talked with him. The Merry Men was a small troupe of five players, but this suited Benny very well. He and Gladys would need to work together for at least a couple of seasons before they would be ready to meet the kind of competition Benny had in mind.

Arthur Lansbury knew Benny's work and he was impressed with Gladys'. He told Benny that he would take them both into the Merry Men if they wished to come. The Merry Men would not go on the road until November, but as Arthur had no Christmas pantomime commitments, his show would stay out throughout the winter. This was fine. The Larks were not due to finish at the Arboretum until the end of the first week of September, and so the Merry Men's late start was an advantage that would give Benny and Gladys that much longer to rehearse.

Benny next concerned himself with material. Light comedians have to be versatile people, and during his years in the business Benny had played in a wide variety of acts. He made a list of the sketches he knew for two players that would be suitable for Gladys and himself—several would have to be worked up for the Merry Men, so as to have program changes ready. It never occurred to Benny to worry about copyright. Actually, most of the material was long since past copyrighting, but even the newer sketches were largely in the public domain. Concert party folk consider that, once a sketch has been performed, it is anyone's to use.

When he had everything prepared, Benny invited Gladys out to dinner.

10

THE invitation threw all three Miller sisters into consternation. "What d'you suppose he's asking you out *for?*" Blanche wanted to know.

"The pleasure of her company, of course," Lily answered, adding, "You *are* lucky, Glad!"

Gladys said: "What can I wear?"

The family stared bleakly at the only two dresses Gladys owned.
"The black," Lily said. "It lies on you so nice."

"It's tight."

"Better the green then," Blanche advised. "Safer."

"No, Glad, definitely the black." Lily was the family authority on clothes. "I'll lend you my beads."

"What about a hat?"

"No hat. People don't eat in hats at night."

"How do you know?"

"I read it in a book." By book, Lily meant a magazine.

"The black it is, then," Gladys said. "And no hat, and your beads, thanks, Lil. Lordy! I hope the menu isn't in French or anything."

"Well, don't be so fashed you don't notice what goes on," Blanche told her. "Me and Lily'll want to hear every word that happens. We shan't go to sleep till you come in."

Benny had asked Gladys where she would like to dine, and then wished he hadn't—she chose the Palais de Danse. The Palais served food, but it was indifferent food, and a dance hall is hardly the best place in which to discuss business. However, Gladys did not know that business was the evening's objective, and there was nothing for Benny to do but to take her dancing.

The Palais was very crowded by the time Gladys and her escort arrived there, after the Larks' evening show in the Arboretum. A number of girls were dancing together, in costumes that ranged from sweaters and skirts to evening gowns. Groups of boys, wearing what seemed to be a uniform of white shirts, dark ties, gray flannel trousers and blazers, stood in groups at the sides of the dance floor. They watched the girls, and occasionally, when an "Excuse Me" dance was announced, they cut in on one of the couples. The music was continuous; when the band needed a rest, a man at a small organ took over.

A brightly lighted table at the end of the dance floor was cleared for Gladys and Benny, and a stained menu card, on which almost everything had been crossed off, was placed before them. Benny did not apologize—he could see from Gladys' face that she would be perfectly happy with a dish of baked nails. Benny wondered for a moment whether perhaps he had better not let the whole partnership idea drop. He had no wish to become seriously involved with an emotional teenager, however talented she might be. But it was only a momentary thought. He was, by now, too much interested in his plans to want to give them up.

Meanwhile, Gladys could not believe that she was awake. Never in her life had she expected to be dining alone with Benny Buckell, and here she was in this lovely romantic setting. Across from the band (five elderly men in pale blue flannel suits piped with pink) was a fountain on which colored lights played; Japanese lanterns hung from the ceiling, and in the center of each table there was a vase containing a single carefully dusted pink wax rose.

Benny and Gladys ate tomato soup, sardines on toast and vanilla ice cream with cocoa sauce. They danced several times. Gladys, as Benny knew from the show, danced well. She was light on her feet, quick to respond, and exactly the right height for him. Presently, while they were sipping the cups of weak coffee that had been brought them, Benny told Gladys about his scheme. He described everything in detail, the finances (it was to be a fifty-fifty arrangement), even the towns the Merry Men expected to play. She did not say anything at first. She seemed so completely taken aback that the thought shot through Benny's mind that she was going to refuse. She said: "When you say a partnership, what d'you mean exactly—d'you mean like the Lansburys have?"

Benny grinned with relief. "Sort of like that, yes," he said.

She beamed at him. "I think that would be wonderful, but what about my sisters?"

"What about them?"

"Well, you see—we don't want to be separated."

Benny said patiently: "My dear, you can't go through life as a posse of five, however fond of each other you are."

Gladys laughed. "It would be nice if we could though, wouldn't it?"

This apparently was her way of turning down his offer. Benny suddenly felt desperate. "Would you feel the same if we made it a threesome?" he said. "You *and Lily* and me in an act together?"

Gladys looked almost as astonished by this offer as Benny felt.

"Why no, of course not," she said. "But I wouldn't dream of such a thing. It would upset all your plans."

It would indeed. There had been quite enough work ahead of them in the first place. "Leave it to me," Benny said. "I'll think, and then I'll talk to Arthur."

They danced again. The management dimmed the lights to a distressing blue, and Gladys closed her eyes. The Variety Three, Benny thought, that's what we'll call it, and it may very well turn out to be better than a double act would have been anyway. One can do more with three, even though Lily doesn't have much to offer.

The other men held their girls close. Benny said: "We'll have to find a place to rehearse. There'll be a lot to do."

Gladys floated in his arms. "We could use the bar at home," she answered. "Dad don't open till noon, and he shuts from two to six. It's got a piano. Would you come? To Tor, I mean?"

"That would be very convenient," Benny replied.

Benny's scheme was not wholly a selfish one. It is true that he meant to further his own career by it, but he also intended to make Gladys a present of all the knowledge he had spent thirty-three years acquiring, and a man cannot be born into a business without absorbing things experience alone could never provide. It is foolish to try to apportion credit for anyone's success, but Benny Buckell taught Gladys Miller more of her job than any other one person.

When Gladys came in that night, both sisters were waiting up.

"Tell us everything, Glad, right from the start," Lily said.

Gladys' report would have astonished Benny Buckell. "He wants to marry me," she said, "though he hasn't actually said so—not yet."

The sisters gasped. "What *did* he say?"

"He said he wanted him and me to go into a partnership like the Lansburys."

"Well, they're certainly married," Blanche commented. "Funny way to put it though, wasn't it."

"He didn't want Glad to rebuff his advances," Lily suggested.

Blanche hugged her sister. "Oh, Glad! It'll be another of your dreams come true, won't it? Just fancy—*Mrs. Benny Buckell!*"

Lily wasn't satisfied. "You *want* to marry him, Glad?" she asked.

"What a daft question, Lil. I've had nobody else on my mind since the first minute I saw him. I was struck all of a heap tonight when I realized what he was sayin'. Couldn't say a word to begin with."

Lily nodded. "That's love, all right. Well, mind you don't rush his declaration. He's got to think he thought of it all himself."

"He can't do that—I've had the idea too long already. But I'll try.

I'll watch myself." Gladys threw herself on her bed. It did not occur to her to mention that Lily was also involved in Benny's plans. "Oh, *how* am I going to bear it? God is too good to us, isn't He, Blanche?"

"He certainly is," Blanche said. "You go out and get practically married, and He even holds that tight old dress of yours together. It ain't split at all."

11

For the Larks' final performance of the Derby Arboretum season, all seats were sold out days in advance, and the standing room on both lawns was crowded. "Auld Lang Syne" was sung, Joe made a speech, Mae wept and everyone in the company received presents of candy and flowers. Then the whole troupe was whisked away to the Royal Hotel, where the Derby Parks Department plied them with supper, dance music, more speeches and beer.

Gladys had her first dance of the evening with Cookie. "I'm going to miss you this winter like bloody anything," he told her cheerfully. "But I think we're going to see each other next year."

"How, Cookie? Tell me."

"Joe's as pleased as Punch with the way you done, and he's going to ask you back to the Larks next year, only don't tell him I told you. He thinks the war'll be over by then, and if it is, Skunby'll be open again. You ain't ever played there, you see."

"I don't think I could play at Skunby," Gladys said. "That's where I made such a mess of the talent competition."

"Nobody remembers that except you. But if you're superstitious, it won't be the same theater. The one you was in was bombed— a proper mess, I can tell you. The new theater ain't built yet, but it's to have padded seats, and a safety curtain and *four* dressing rooms. So the Queen of Song'll be able to have one all to herself if she wants it, bless her."

Gladys sighed. "Makes you drool, don't it?"

They danced for a while in silence. Then Cookie said: "Benny was tellin' me about teamin' up with you and Lily. You girls have made quite a hit there."

"Yes."

"You'll learn a lot."

"Yes."

"But take a tip from an old friend, Gladdie. Keep that schoolgirl crush of yours within bounds."

"Cookie! Don't you realize—"

"I don't realize anything. I'm only tellin' you for your own good. But then I'm jealous, I expect."

"Of me?"

"No, silly, him. If you must lose your head over a man old enough to be your father, what's wrong with yours truly? I'm not such a bad-lookin' fellow, not when I got me back to the light."

12

THE next day, Benny Buckell accompanied the three Miller sisters to The Nag's Head. He stayed with them there two weeks. His visit caused Holly some exertion, for although she had never made any special preparations when Cookie came home with the girls, she felt different about Benny Buckell. Her efforts to be a tidy housekeeper consisted mainly of hiding things, and she also raised the family's standard of living. ("Why are there two dishes of margarine on the table?" Flo asked at breakfast on Benny's first morning. "There are not," Holly replied, glowering. "*One* is butter.")

Entertaining Benny was no problem. He and Gladys and Lily rehearsed all day long. Benny had worked out a program for the Variety Three with which Gladys was impressed, Lily dazzled and Arthur Lansbury satisfied. It included sketches, songs, some dancing and ukulele playing for all of them. Benny also played his violin and Lily began to learn the accordion, with the idea of making it her "speciality". Everything they did was new to the two girls, and they had a great deal to memorize, but Gladys found, just as Cookie had said, that she learned a lot besides the acts themselves. Benny not only knew his own job, he knew how to help the sisters with theirs. He was patient, kind and encouraging and, feeling toward him the way she did, it was not difficult for Gladys to take pains to please him. When they were not actually going over their lines, the members of the Variety Three talked and thought about their work, or they listened to the comments of the Miller family, a permanent and critical audience.

Benny had expected the Millers to take an interest in the act; what he had not expected was to find himself rapidly becoming fond of the Millers. Within a few days after his arrival in Tor, he was caught up, like a fly in a spider web, in the warmth and friendliness they wrapped around him. It was a long time since Benny Buckell had had anything more than a boardinghouse room for a home, and he had forgotten what home life could be like; when, at the end of a fortnight, he had to go away to fulfill a two weeks' engagement at a vaudeville house in Newcastle, he was extremely reluctant to go.

The family greatly enjoyed his visit. Benny had helped around the inn whenever he could, he had turned his charm full on for the benefit of the Millers' friends, he had gone out of his way to amuse Gladys' little sisters, and he had flirted mildly with Holly. With two exceptions, Tor village, which did not take readily to strangers, had been pleased to accept, even welcome, Benny Buckell. The exceptions were Fred Miller and Martin Hay. Fred said to Holly after Benny's first evening at the inn: "This Buckell fellow—he's too old for our Glad. Can't be a day younger than Cookie, and you weren't havin' none of *him*."

"Benny's quite a different sort," Holly said comfortably. "He's not young, I grant you that, but he don't seem his age, and Glad's devoted to him."

"As any blind pussy can see." Fred wasn't happy, though. "Fellow puts on airs," he complained.

"Benny don't put on airs, Fred! He's a man of ambition, that's all. There's no law against 'avin' ambition, that I know of."

"Oh yes, there is. What's it say int' Catechism? 'Do your duty in that state of life in which it shall please God to call you.'"

If Benny Buckell was Glad's idea of lifelong happiness, he would try to like him. Fred sighed, though, when it occurred to him that four more men he didn't readily take to might be joining the family in the capacity of son-in-law one day, all of them, maybe, sprouting little blond mustaches.

Martin Hay merely thought Benny a bore, but then neither Martin nor Fred was female, and eighteen years old.

During Benny's absence in Newcastle, Gladys and Lily worked at their sketches and songs. Gladys found the going fairly easy, Lily did not. ("The only way to improve your memory is to learn plenty by heart *every day*," Benny had said. "Yes," Gladys added, "it don't matter what—the beer prices, the Bible, anything you can lay your hands on.")

Benny returned from Newcastle in mid-October, to find the village of Tor bathed in warm sunshine and lying under a cloudless sky. This was Indian summer weather, as rare and unexpected as it was welcome, and the whole village came out on holiday. There were blackberrying parties up on the moors and, although the cricket season was officially over, cricket matches were played in the long meadow in the valley. In the late afternoon, for an hour before dark, the Tor and New Cut Glee Club sang from the gibbet steps. Benny arrived early in the morning on the third day of this unusual weather, just in time for a Miller family swimming picnic.

He did not want to go. Even though the sun was glorious, there had been no time for it to warm the river, and a dip in the icy Thorne was not at all Benny's idea of pleasure. But the Millers were so delighted with the plans they had made, and so pleased that he had arrived in time for them and before the weather broke, that he had not the heart to refuse their invitation. Their happiness at having him with them again touched him: they seemed genuinely eager to make him feel that he belonged.

Fred, as he always seemed able to do in an emergency (and good weather in Tor was certainly that), arranged for a friend to handle the noon opening hours at the inn, so the picnic party was able to leave The Nag's Head by eleven o'clock. A large meal in heavy containers accompanied them, each member of the family carrying what he could. The particular swimming hole that the Millers had in mind was about two miles upstream. One reached it by a winding, awkward path on which nobody but Benny slipped. He was soon exhausted by the walk, and amazed that the Millers, usually such sensible people, should go to so much trouble in pursuit of discomfort. But when he arrived, he had to admit that the picnic spot they had chosen was a perfect one. The swimming hole was smaller than he had expected, but it was deep and clear, there were good rocks for diving from, and, farther up, a shallow place that was excellent for paddling. Beside the water was a wide, grassy plot, flat and just right for picnicking. Back of it, the hillside, sparsely covered with trees and clumps of tall bushes, rose steeply.

Holly paddled while the girls undressed behind the bushes on the hill; Benny and Fred changed under the trees at the water's edge. Fred was ready in no time, in a little pair of faded cotton shorts that had seen better days many years ago. (His best pair, bright blue wool and scarcely worn, had been lent to Benny.)

Somewhat to Benny's surprise, none of the Miller girls could swim, but Fred dived beautifully. He went in over and over again, a concentrated expression on his face, every dive neat, quiet and a joy to watch. He was still busy diving when Benny (the last to go in and the first to come out) had dressed and joined Holly on the picnic lawn. She had lunch all ready, and a teakettle bubbling on a little Primus stove. Lily and the two youngest Millers were beside her, clamoring for food. Gladys and Blanche were nowhere to be seen. Holly said: "Benny, do go up the hill and tell the girls to hurry! It always takes them so long to dress, and I don't want to eat till they come. We never wait for Fred."

Benny nodded, and strolled up the hill in the direction of the girls' voices. He lit a cigarette. Now that his swim was behind him, he felt relaxed and refreshed. He thought affectionately, and a little enviously, of the Millers. One would be safe against almost anything if one belonged in a group as united as they were.

Because of the tall bushes, Benny was soon out of sight of the lawn and the swimming hole, but never out of the sunshine for long—the beams fell sharply. He made no noise as he climbed. Gladys and Blanche were easy enough to find—one just followed the sound of their laughter. Without calling to them, Benny parted the branches. Gladys and Blanche were just ahead, Blanche in her petticoat and Gladys naked. Gladys' black hair hung down loose over her shoulders and in the sharpness of the sunlight that enveloped her, she looked as poised and graceful as a tall white bird. Benny saw the girls only a second before they saw him; the branches rustled as he parted them. Blanche gave a little scream and grabbed a towel, but Gladys showed no surprise at all. She smiled happily at him, and waved.

That evening, Benny led Gladys out of the crowded Nag's Head into the garden and asked her to marry him. She said yes at once, weeping and clinging to him in a kind of desperation, as if he had kept her waiting for this a long while. So he did not tell her that until that morning nothing had been further from his thoughts than matrimony, nor that only that morning had she become as precious and desirable to him as he apparently already was to her.

13

THAT night, there were celebrations at The Nag's Head Inn. It surprised Benny that the news of the engagement was not more of a surprise to the Millers—the champagne was so ready to hand and so speedily produced that Fred might have had advance warning of the announcement. The champagne was for family consumption —wellwishers in the bar were treated to beer. Everybody kissed everybody several times and Fred decided, after one look at his daughter's radiant face, that he must have been wrong in his estimation of Benny Buckell. Anyone who could make Gladys look the way she did tonight deserved the warmest welcome he could give him. When he said as much to Holly, she replied: "Nonsense, Fred! Glad only looks the way I did once, a long time ago."

Up in the girls' bedroom, the sisters talked until the small hours of the morning. "What sort of a wedding will you have, Glad? You thought?" Lily asked.

"Of course I've thought," Gladys replied. "I've had it planned for months. I'm going to have everything the way Margaret Leake did—marquee and all."

Long after the rest of the household was sleeping, Benny Buckell tossed and turned on his hard mattress in the tiny, windowless bedroom normally reserved for the use of commercial travelers. His head ached and his stomach troubled him, though not because of Mr. Miller's good wine. Benny was worried. Something should have been said this evening (at least by this evening—earlier would have been better) which had not been said. At all costs the Millers must be told first thing in the morning, and when told, Gladys and her family were likely to be very much upset.

The Millers and the people like the Millers are the guardians of the British social code. Their standards are rigid. They treat marriage in much the same way that they treat a puppy—when it is new, they watch over it closely and keep after it, so that by the time it is grown, it is not only housebroken and manageable, but full of indescribable rewards. If, however, their marriages fail, they do not abandon them. They do what they can with what they have. To an Englishman, any dog is better than no dog at all.

So when Benny Buckell told the Millers that he had been divorced eight years ago, and that his former wife was still living (she had a job in Sheffield, he said) he distressed them deeply. Their minds were filled with one thought, and one thought only—Gladys would not now be able to have a church wedding. (On the back cover of every issue of *The Tor and New Cut Parish Magazine* there appeared the following statements: "Divorced Persons may not be married in Church. Confetti may not be thrown anywhere.") In England, marriages may not be solemnized in private homes; the only alternative to the church ceremony is the civil, Registry Office, one.

Benny broke his news to the Millers at breakfast, not the best of times, but he was afraid that if he waited longer, his small stock of courage would fail him. When he had finished what he had to say, nobody spoke. Flo, thinking of her bridesmaid's dress, began to cry.

That morning, the inn, usually so noisy whether the bar was open or not, was as quiet as a morgue. Holly and her four younger daughters huddled upstairs in the girls' bedroom. Fred shuffled about among the rabbit hutches. Benny and Gladys sat in the kitchen. Benny said: "I'm terribly sorry, Glad. I know I should have told you sooner."

Gladys shook her head. "There wasn't any need." She nodded in the direction of the staircase. "They'll get over it, you'll see."

"I'm not worried about *them*. What about you?"

"Well—" Gladys' unwhitened sandals slipped off. She rubbed one bare foot against the other. "It's always been Mum's theory that we can't none of us have everything we'd like, and this is one of those times for me. I don't *really* mind—only I'd sort of set my heart on a white dress, and a big fuss."

"Darling! You shall have the white dress and the fuss, and the church too, damn it, if I can get it for you. How much does it cost?"

"Seven-and-six. But not if you're divorced."

"How much is it then?"

"*Bribe* Mr. Hay?" Gladys laughed. "I wouldn't dream of trying that, even if I thought we could succeed. No, Benny. We can stick by the rules. Only you'll just have to show a bit of patience while we do our minding. Give us till teatime and we'll be over it."

They were. Holly was the first to recover, and when Holly decided to cheer up, everybody else had to cheer up too. "You give over frettin'," she said firmly to her eldest daughter. "It's like I said—nobody can have everything exactly how they wants it. You couldn't have a finer husband than Benny, and look what you got besides! Dad, and me, and the girls."

Now that he had, as it were, broken the ice, Benny wanted to tell Gladys about his first marriage. He felt that she had a right to know, and it disappointed him when he found that she wasn't interested. "Your past is your business," she said, "not mine. I don't care if you've had five wives—or ten."

"I know, and I'm proud you feel like that," Benny answered. "All the same—"

"Well, all right, if you must!" Gladys said, but her attitude discouraged him. He found Holly more sympathetic.

Later, Holly said to her husband, "Do you remember, Fred, what I told you about Benny being ambitious? Well, it was *that* that ruined his first marriage. Janey (that was her name, Janey) wanted him to take any job that came along, but Benny had his pride, and he held out till he could get the right kind of work."

"Does he keep her?"

"Keep who?"

"His wife. The one he divorced. Does he pay for her keep?"

"Dear me, no. She has a job."

"What she do?" Fred asked.

"She's a manicurist."

"A *what*?"

"She clips other women's nails."

"Does she, now!" Fred exclaimed. "In this village, it's only horses that needs help with that."

Tongues wagged in New Cut and Tor over Gladys Miller's plans for a Registry Office wedding. The news took everyone by surprise, including Lady Leake. "Couldn't you have done something for the child?" she said to the rector the next time he dined with her. "People do, you know. We had a rector here once who made quite a fetish of marrying divorcees. He used to get special permission from the bishop."

"Special permission," Martin replied, "predicates special cases, and from what I've seen of Mr. Benny Buckell, he looks like an all-too-common occurrence to me."

"Well, perhaps," Lady Leake said, "but the Millers are such *good* folk, it does seem hard."

Martin helped himself to another potato. "So far, the Millers haven't asked me to perform this marriage," he said. "When and if they do, I shall refuse, and then give them all my reasons. D'you want to hear them?"

Lady Leake looked shocked. "Good gracious, no! I was only surprised because I thought Gladys Miller was your pet."

"She is."

"And, of course, having traveled so much, I don't feel as strongly about divorce as you do."

But the Millers never did consult the rector. They knew what the rules of their church were and, being a law-abiding family, it did not occur to any of them to ask to have exceptions made in their favor. When people commiserated with Holly, she said: "Well, yes. We'd all have liked a church wedding, but as Fred and I tell Gladys, rules is rules, and we wouldn't have no respect for Mr. Hay if he didn't keep 'em. We're planning a party after the ceremony just the same, though, and we're *countin'* on you bein' able to come. . . ."

14

GLADYS and Benny were married on the morning of November 11, which turned out to be Armistice Day. The bride wore pale blue silk, a large hat and shiny black patent-leather shoes. Afterward, Gladys could not help thinking that the ceremony reminded her more than anything of a visit to the dentist. The Registrar's Office was in a dingy red brick building in the business section of Chesterfield, and the Millers, who arrived much too early (they had been lent a Model T Ford for the occasion) had to sit for nearly an hour in a dark waiting room while several other couples were united. The waiting room was furnished with large leather chairs, a calendar published by a life insurance company and back numbers of illustrated magazines. The sisters all wore gardenia corsages. The smell of hers made Flo sick.

Outside, the streets of the town were filled with school-children marching in procession, and detachments of Boy Scouts, and brass bands. It was impossible to shut out the sounds of national rejoicing. When finally Benny and Gladys were summoned before the registrar's table (the witnesses to the marriage were friends from Tor—the Tolmans and the Crews), the town celebrations had reached such a height that it was difficult to hear what was being said, and Gladys had hardly realized that the ceremony had begun, before she discovered that it was over.

When the wedding party returned to Tor, they found that the turmoil of Armistice Day was in full swing there, too. Martin had held a thanksgiving service at the gibbet steps, the manager of the Halesowen Company had made a speech, and now people were dancing in the lane outside The Nag's Head, waiting for Fred to open up.

In the end, the whole neighborhood joined in the Miller wedding celebrations. Nobody knew who was toasting Gladys and who was toasting peace. Fred sold a great deal of beer and gave away even more. A homemade cake of vast proportions was cut and handed round, telegrams were opened—one from the Lansburys read "LIFELONG FELICITATIONS"; another, signed Cookie, said "YOUR NEWS SAVED BREATH WAS ABOUT SUGGEST YOU MARRY ME."

At four in the afternoon, the Model T was pulled out again and the bride and groom, accompanied by all the Millers, drove to Manley railway station. Everyone sang, and when the train came in, Holly tried to dance the highland fling. Gladys looked at Benny and noticed that his face seemed unfamiliar and curiously blurred. She wondered if everyone else's head ached as badly as her own.

Finally, and at long last, in a small, ill-ventilated first-class carriage, Benny and Gladys found themselves alone. They were to spend their honeymoon in Manchester, and in four days' time, meet Lily in Preston and join the Merry Men. Fortunately the distance between Manley and Manchester is not great, for Gladys wept most of the way, partly because of her aching head and the nearness of her beloved, but mostly because of that age-old custom which decrees that when a girl goes away with her husband, she leaves her parents and her sisters behind.

Part IV

1

From Mrs. Benny Buckell to Mrs. Fred Miller:
SETTLE, YORKSHIRE.
November 20, 1918

DEAR MUM,

I got the washing all right thanks I was ever so pleased to see the old slippers. Them fancy wedding shoes still don't fit though I cut the sides down like you said and now they flap when I walk I shall buy a new pair if I ever get the chance which don't seem likely as at time of writing. The Merry Men keeps us on the go worse than the Larks I think but who am I to complain the show's doing fine we get good houses everywhere. With the soldiers coming home I expect they'd like us even if we did nothing at all and nothing we certainly do not.

I never told you what happened to our honeymoon did I well I'm still looking for it. You remember Arthur wired Lily to come to Preston sooner the opening date being put forward well he wired us to. There was the telegram waiting when we got to Manchester Benny never should of told Arthur where we was. So we cancel our lovely place at the hotel (we had two rooms one just for bath imagine). We got to Preston no supper around midnight. Arthur had booked for us at a boardinghouse over a shop Brothwell Tobacconist what a place to take a bride I did laugh. Next day we find Lily all right and Benny bought roses he felt bad about the no own bath but I said whats it matter just so we got own bed.

I suppose I'll get used to being Mrs. Buckell one day.

There's six of us in the Merry Men one more than last year Mr. and Mrs. Arthur Benny Lily Me and Billie Whittington the Personality Plus Girl. Billie contortions lovely legs you never know where her head is going to pop out next. Well I must bring this to a close I try not to think of you too often as in spite of being so closely associated with the one I adore I miss you all terrible.

Lovingly,
GLAD

From Mrs. Benny Buckell to Mr. Fred Miller:

LOW GILL, WESTMORELAND
December 27, 1918

DEAR DAD,

Yes it was awful missing Christmas at home I knew it would be. How is your flu getting on how lucky Blanche is home this winter I said all along that Joe managed the Larks without her till he had her so why not again.

I filled one of Benny's socks with sweets Christmas Eve but it hung next the gas ring and some of the sweets melted Benny wasn't so pleased they was his best.

Arthur Lansbury isn't as much fun as Joe to work with he gets terrible stage fright poor little man can't eat and takes snuff his clothes is covered with it. Mrs. Arthur is our pianist we have to take tempo from her she nods her head while playing and we watch the top.

Well Dad don't go trying to get to work too soon I'm glad Rose is back she sent a nice card saying she been demobbed.

Lovingly,

GLAD

From Mrs. Benny Buckell to Miss Flo Miller:

SHAP, WESTMORELAND
January 2, 1919

DEAR FLO,

We got the lovely picture of you in your ballet dress and Benny says to tell you no wonder you was clapped for at the Welfare concert. You look as pretty as anything and when Benny says that it means something he likes pretty girls and has met a lot. Mum wrote us about the dancing school opening in Manley and if you'd like lessons Benny and me will buy you a set also will pay bus fares and any extras Benny says schools always think up some.

If you want the lessons go and see about them *at once* so you start before your legs addle most begin younger than ten.

Lovingly,

GLAD

Part IV

From John Cook to Gladys Buckell:
WARBLINGTON, YORKSHIRE
February 2, 1919

DEAR GLAD,
    You're a fine one expecting a concert party pianist to write letters while on tour. By the time I finish this trip I probably won't have hands to hold a beer mug with, let alone a pen. We've had quite a time one way and another. Mae's been out of voice several times and I had to set her songs where she could get to them. She hated that. The old man's in fine shape though and just as fond as ever of rehearsing all day long with yours truly wearing the piano stool out.
    Am sending you some Glitter Dust (spangle your own clothes) I got two pots cheap. Tell Benny to take good care of you. Remember I get to marry you next time.
Love,
COOKIE

Telegram to Buckell, Merry Men Company, Pavilion Theater, Cockermouth, Cumberland:
March 10, 1919
CAN OFFER YOUR ACT SUMMER SEASON SKUNBY SIXTEEN WEEKS EIGHTEEN POUNDS PER WEEK REPLY LANSBURY SKUNBY-ON-SEA.

Telegram to Lansbury, Skunby-on-Sea:
YOUR OFFER ACCEPTED. BUCKELL.

2

THE Lansbury Larks' new theater at Skunby-on-Sea was the usual oblong shape inside, but the building in which it was housed was circular. It stood at the end of the pier where the old bombed theater had been, but was upstairs, over some gift and candy shops, a fortuneteller's, and a glassed-in tearoom looking out to sea. A broad flight of wooden steps on the landward side led up to the main entrance, and a narrow stair on the seaward side, outside the teashop, led up to the stage door. The theater had four dressing rooms, no water, a safety curtain and six hundred leatherette-covered tip-up seats.

Skunby had been hard at work all winter, pulling up the barbed wire entanglements that the army had left behind, rebuilding and renovating. Notices were posted warning visitors to keep a lookout for floating mines. Martello towers (concrete gun emplacements modeled after towers built along the south coast of England during the Napoleonic wars) stood at intervals along the shore and, as these were too solid to remove easily, Skunby left them where they were and made picnic spots of them. There was a lot to do, and the work was nowhere near finished by Whitsun week end, when the first wave of summer visitors arrived. While the residents hammered and painted, and rolled and rerolled the bowling greens, the tourists flocked into town, overflowing the hotels and the boardinghouses and even the shelters on the promenade. They came from all over the North Midlands of England and they were as happy as children let out of school to see the sea again. They paddled and swam and sand sailed, they rode on everything in the fun fair that was ready for them to ride on, and they made jokes about the floating mines. ("Don't tha go standin' on thy head int' water, Ma! Happen tha might find fire brigade draggin' thee out in a net. . . .") They bought quantities of knickknacks from the shiny little gift shops, and far more candy than they could decently consume, and night after night they filled the Lansbury Larks' new theater, where an aging pierrot sang:

> I have led a good life, full of peace and quiet,
> But I shall have an old age steeped in rum and riot;
> I have been a nice lad, careful of my morals—
> I shall be a grandad full of vice and quarrels. . . .
>
> I have been a sweet boy, wed to peace and study;
> But I shall have an old age ribald, coarse and bloody—
> With white hair and red face—full of hell and liquor—
> When I get a bad thought I shall let her flicker. . . .

Joe had dreamed all winter about the Skunby summer opening, and watched excitedly as his theater took shape. This year, he had planned his programs and engaged his company with more than usual care, and yet for the first time he found his work taxing—he felt tired all day long. So he decided that, instead of the whole company remaining on the stage in full view of the audience throughout the show, only those artistes would appear who were actually in the number being performed. This gave Joe a chance for an occasional offstage rest, and it pleased the Larks because now they sometimes had an opportunity to hold the stage alone. One change in the company saddened Joe: Mae Lansbury was no longer a regular member of the troupe. Her singing voice had almost gone. Every now and again throughout the summer, more to please Joe than herself, Mae would appear with the Larks as a special guest, but these occasions were not happy. Skunby's postwar crowds were not accustomed to Mae's style; they were embarrassed by the cracked-voiced old lady in her gloves and feathers and trailing low-cut gowns.

But they loved Gladys Miller. Joe gave Gladys some of Mae's sentimental songs to sing:

>'Tis drear to be alone,
>In this vast world of ours;
>All nature seems in love,
>E'en to the simple flowers;
>The waves that kiss the shore,
>The stars that deck the sky,
>All teach 'tis sweet to love,
>Then why not you and I?

Fortunately for Joe (they would have proved too much for him) the Lark Walks were no longer permitted—there was now too much traffic on Skunby's roads. So Joe devoted almost the whole of his morning and afternoon shows to the children. As before, these sessions were held outdoors, but on the pier instead of the beach. Beside the new theater, inside a canvas enclosure, a small stage was erected, and deck chairs placed before it. The daytime shows (they took place at eleven and half-past three) lasted an hour, and cost sixpence. If it rained, cast and audience moved upstairs under cover, into the Larks' main theater.

Except at the height of the wasp season (with so many open candy stalls, the wasps enjoyed Skunby pier as much as anyone) Gladys loved working outdoors. She felt much more a part of the holiday crowd when she was out in the sun and wind with them, even though it was tiring to have to shout to make herself heard. Benny resented the distractions. Hardly would a show have started before a pleasure steamer might arrive at the pier head, and disembark her passengers immediately behind the stage, or a sailing boat, fully rigged, might go by, causing everybody in the audience to forget the sweating pierrots. A couple of times a month, Skunby held lifeboat practice, an event heralded by the firing of a rocket from a point that seemed to be immediately below the front row of deck chairs. This would be followed by the grinding of hydraulic doors (the boathouse was underneath the pier) and then the lifeboat, fully manned, would plop with a great splash into the sea just ahead. By this time, most of the Larks' audience would be hanging over the side of the pier, and there it would remain until the lifeboat was out of sight.

Joe's company this year, in addition to stage manager Blanche and three locally recruited stagehands, consisted of himself, Cookie, Gladys, Benny Buckell, Lily Miller and a couple of dancing girls who called themselves the Two-Step Sisters. Joe missed Mae sadly, but otherwise he was very pleased with his troupe. The Variety Three was popular. Joe was amazed at how much Lily had improved since last year; she played the accordion quite well now, and she and Gladys had a nice little song together that concerned two quarreling children:

> I don't want to play in your yard,
> I don't like you any more;
> You'll be sorry when you see me
> Sliding down our cellar door.
>
> You can't holler down our rain barrel,
> You can't climb our apple tree;
> I don't want to play in your yard
> If you won't be good to me. . . .

With Mae out of the company, Gladys' status in the Lansbury Larks changed. She was no longer the butt of Joe's teasing—the Two-Step Sisters (their names were Gracie and Anne) had replaced her. Gracie and Anne were not related in real life, but they were the same height and size, flat-chested, with bright blond curls, and the same apparent ability to tap ceaselessly in their clattery little shoes.

"See them two blondes?" Joe would ask the audience. "The blond part ain't real, of course. You put it on with a toothbrush. Not a new toothbrush, mind—that is, unless you want the new toothbrush to lose all its bristles. That's what's goin' to 'appen to these girls soon. Any day now they'll 'ave 'eads as fluffy as billiard balls. . . ."

Gladys came in for different treatment from Mae Lansbury too. Up to now, the Queen of Song had treated her like a child. Marriage changed that. As a married woman, Gladys found herself privy to quite another Mae Lansbury, a knowing, winking Mae who poked her in the ribs when she wanted to emphasize the point of a bawdy story, and pressed upon her invitations to join a tea and gossip circle that seemed to meet all day long at the Lansbury bungalow. Mae's lady friends had three topics of conversation: sex, pregnancy and operations. After a session at Mae's, Gladys sometimes found it difficult to look Joe Lansbury in the eye, for Mae, having experienced neither motherhood nor surgery, felt it incumbent upon her (like the people of Tor with their weather) to make the most of what she had.

Once the Larks' summer show was safely launched, the company found time to enjoy itself between performances, swimming and sand sailing and riding the fun fair's little two-seater roller-coaster cars. The only Lark who didn't have as good a time as she had hoped was Blanche. The Reverend Fox, though back in Skunby and full of zeal, had changed his field of endeavor. Instead of conducting beach services in damp, sandy pews, he organized "faith teas" in the Palm Lounge of the Grand Hotel. The teas, accompanied by hot buttered crumpets and éclairs that disgorged artificial cream, cost one-and-sixpence per person and included light orchestral music and a brief prayer. Blanche, who liked her religion inexpensive and jolly, was discouraged by the turn things had taken, but Lily was impressed, and attended the faith teas several times. The Reverend Fox had put on a good deal of weight during the war, Blanche noticed, and although he could still draw crowds, they were not the same crowds as before, being older, richer and on the whole cleaner than the Young Christian Army had been. But as

Lily pointed out, you couldn't expect everything, and what was lost in comfort was certainly gained in class.

3

GLADYS and Benny roomed at Mrs. Pegler's nearly all summer. At first they rented a furnished apartment, but Gladys was totally miscast in the role of housekeeper, and although she was an excellent cook, she had such wildly extravagant ideas that neither of them could afford this method of living for long. Benny, a fastidious man, was appalled when he found a piece of lipstick in the butter ("Why, so there is, love!" Gladys had cried. "And no good for anything now, either. It's all squashed.") Once they moved to Mrs. Pegler's, however, the Buckells were much better off, for life at The Dunes was in a way very like life at The Nag's Head—both were places of ease and song, as any house became once it had Millers in it. The sisters (Lily and Blanche boarded at The Dunes too) had little regard for the privacy of anyone. If Benny wanted to be alone with his wife, he had to lock their bedroom door, and even then his relatives were apt to come pounding and shouting to be admitted. Only by making rules at the top of his voice about not touching his possessions was Benny able to keep track of anything he owned. And yet he did not really mind. He was aware that in marrying a Miller sister, he had married the Miller family too, and that belonging, like everything else, has its price.

But Benny would have been a great deal happier if he could have understood his wife's views about her work. He had already gathered that she did not share his ambition, and yet he could not make out how an artiste who set as high standards for herself as Gladys did could *not* be ambitious. The casual, easygoing manner that made her so delightful on the stage was far from being the informal thing it seemed—every look, every phrase, every move was carefully studied in front of a mirror, and then rehearsed and re-rehearsed before Benny and the others. Mostly Benny knew better than Gladys did how to achieve the results she wanted, but if Gladys felt sure she was right, nothing he could say could move her. ("No, Benny, I'm sorry, it's no good your way. If I don't do it like I showed you, I'll lose the laugh.") He learned to give in to her when this happened, for she usually turned out to be right.

Benny finally decided that Gladys' lack of ambition was a pose, and he did not appreciate the humor of it. Several times during the summer, talent scouts from London theatrical agencies came to see the Lansbury Larks, and these occasions created tension in everybody except Gladys: even the calm-tempered Cookie would be on edge. When it was known that there was a scout in front, Gladys was the only member of the company who gave exactly the same quality of performance that she always gave for, as she said to Benny, how could she do better, when she was already doing her best?

Alone on the stage except for Cookie and his piano, Gladys would sing:

> I'm a maiden who never refuses
> The pleasures that come in my way,
> For now is the time to be merry,
> To be bashful is but to delay,
> When the stars far above us are shining,
> With a party of friends, but a few,
> Quick the night passes by and we finish,
> With oysters and wine at 2,
> Oysters and wine at 2 A.M., 2 A.M., 2 A.M.,
> Oysters and wine at 2 A.M.,
> Oysters and wine at 2. . . .

The scouts seemed to enjoy this number, but none of them came backstage, as Benny hoped they would, to offer the Buckells a London contract.

"You're barmy to mind," Gladys said unfeelingly to her husband. "What do we want with London, and those southern places?"

"Nothing," Benny answered, "nothing at all. What we want is to stay right where we are for the rest of our lives, playing North Midlands concert parties, the Wombshaw pantomime and the pier at Skunby-on-Sea."

His sarcasm was lost on Gladys. "Wombshaw pantomime!" she cried. "Oh Benny, do you think we could?"

Tiresomely, Lily Miller continued to be very ambitious indeed, and smart about it too—so smart that Benny sometimes wondered if he had not married the wrong sister. Lily was not quite fifteen when the 1919 Skunby summer season opened, but she looked more. Lily noticed that artistes advertising in *The Stage* offered among their qualifications "King's English on and off," and so she set to work on her accent. She was determined to achieve, as soon as possible, the bilingual capacity of many concert party performers, who speak their native cockney, Lancashire or Derbyshire dialects, but who produce for stage purposes King's English, or something akin to it. Lily's efforts would have pleased Madame Lola very much. As it was, they pleased Jamie Leake.

Toward the end of July, Lady Leake took a month's lease on a house outside Skunby. This was for Jamie's benefit—Jamie was now home from Switzerland for good, but the doctor had recommended bracing sea air. On the first Sunday that the Leakes were in the town, Lily walked over with a pair of complimentary tickets for the Larks' next show. She looked so grown up, and seemed so self-possessed, that although Jamie did not ask her to stay to tea this time, he talked with her at length and showed her around the house's dried-up garden. Jamie was now twenty—a gentle, charming young man who, when he had seen the Larks once, took to seeing them every evening. Jamie found the society of the pierrots, and particularly pierrette Lily Miller, extremely attractive. He haunted the pier theater almost as faithfully as the young people who wanted Blanche to find jobs for them, though Jamie had no theatrical ambitions. What he enjoyed, after his long experience of sanatoriums, was being where healthy people were having a good time.

Lady Leake was not pleased with her son's predilection for pierrots and the society of an innkeeper's daughter, but then Lady Leake was not pleased with anything much in postwar England. The major part of her income had disappeared in the general inflation, and Leake Revel, as soon as the army moved out, had begun to crack and fall apart even more expensively than it usually did. But in spite of herself Lady Leake could not help liking Lily Miller—she was so extraordinarily respectful, so genuinely admiring not only of the Leake family, but also of their great gaunt home and its stuffy contents. So when Jamie said that he would like to stay at Skunby until the pierrot season ended, Lady Leake agreed to extend their visit, though she was not a woman who enjoyed vacations.

Jamie Leake fell in love with Lily Miller on her fifteenth birthday. Fred and Holly and the two youngest Millers were in Skunby for the occasion; the family celebrated by taking Lily to lunch at the Grand Hotel. ("This all the coffee I get, Lily?" "Yes, Dad. It's a deemid-ass.") The real celebration, however, took place in the evening when, just before the Lansbury Larks' grand finale, Joe took Lily by the hand and led her down to the footlights. He explained to the audience what day it was, and he asked them to accompany the cast in singing "Happy Birthday." Then he invited each member of the audience to strike a match, and hold it aloft. Blanche turned the lights out, and as all sang, tiny points of light flickered all over the theater. Joe whispered to Lily: "I couldn't bake thee a cake, but there's thy candles!" By the time the lights went up again, on a beaming Joe and a weeping Lily, Jamie Leake, in the front row, had already lost his heart.

This summer, Fred hadn't been able to arrange his week's holiday to coincide with those of his bowling partners from before the war, and without them his interest in the game flagged. The men at the greens now seemed to be mostly young fellows whom he didn't fancy playing with, and like Joe Lansbury, Fred found that he didn't feel as vigorous as he used to: even Skunby's bracing air seemed too bracing for comfort. Holly, however, was full of energy. "Come on, Fred!" she called to him one afternoon, after they had already spent more than an hour in the fun fair. "Let's go down the tunnel of love! Benny and Glad's just gone. I see'd 'em."

"Aw, Holly!" he grumbled. "What's the sense? We're already payin' for Mrs. Pegler's best front room."

In the tunnel of love, as their little boat jolted along a green-lit, plywood-enclosed, canal, Gladys and Benny kissed with rapture, to the complete satisfaction of the ticket collector, who liked to see the facilities of the place made use of. Behind them in the next boat, bolt upright and as far apart as the allover coziness of the construction would permit, sat Jamie and Lily. Lastly, wedged tight between two drama students, came Blanche.

Meanwhile, the two youngest Millers were visiting the house of fun. Here there were distortion mirrors, floors that wobbled when you walked on them, sudden drafts that blew your skirt over your head: the place was a riot. At the door, a great papier-mâché clown stood rolling from side to side, as if doubled up with mirth. From somewhere within his body, gale after gale of deafening laughter blared forth.

This summer, Joe again held a children's talent competition, and to Gladys' delight it took place during her family's vacation. Flo Miller won. As Flo pirouetted to victory in the lovely little ballet dress Holly had made for her, a small brown velvet ghost was laid to rest—Posie Wheeler singing "Daddy Wouldn't Buy Me a Bow-Wow."

4

WOMBSHAW is a Derbyshire coal mining town. In addition to its coal mine, it has ironworks and railroad marshaling yards. From the surrounding hills, the town, which straggles over the floor of a valley, is usually hidden from view under a pall of black smoke. The sooty atmosphere makes gardening difficult and whippet racing impossible—the dogs develop rheumy-eye and cannot see properly to run—but other forms of entertainment flourish; there are bowls, billiards, the music hall and (recently) the movies. Once a year, for six weeks after Christmas, Wombshaw's vaudeville house, like the one in Manley, is turned over to pantomime, and a good pantomime it is too, one of the best. People come from all over the neighboring countryside to see it.

Pantomimes, like pierrot shows, date back into history, and they have, for the most part, the same artistes—pierrots make some of their wintertime living by playing in pantomime. All pantomimes follow the same pattern—that of a musical play in verse, based on a nursery rhyme or a fairy tale with a lot of knockabout clowning, followed by a wordless playlet, the Harlequinade, from which pantomime derived its name. The leading players, the Principal Girl and the Principal Boy, are always played by women (the Principal Boy in tights and high-heeled shoes) and the leading comic figure, a middle-aged woman, is always played by a man. None of this is at all confusing to the British mind.

Wombshaw's 1919 Christmas Pantomime was *Cinderella*, with

Benny Buckell and Gladys Miller as the Ugly Sisters, and Lily as Cinderella's mother's personal maid. Alf Hall, the producer, was at first unwilling to take Gladys on—in his memory, Cinderella's Ugly Sisters had always been men—but after Joe Lansbury had talked with him (Joe was playing the Old Woman in *The Old Woman Who Lived in a Shoe* this year) he agreed to give Gladys an audition, and once heard, Gladys was in.

Cinderella was a scintillating show, with more sequins and paste diamonds to the square inch than Gladys had ever seen: Alf liked to give his customers good value. The Principal Boy and the young lady who played her lover had fourteen changes of costume apiece, all but two involving tights and low-cut spangled bodices. Cinderella's coach was drawn onto the stage by four live white ponies, and in the ballroom scene there was a massive gold staircase, with chandeliers swinging precariously above it, and no handrail. As usual, the story was a mixture of several fairy tales. Gladys opened the show:

To practice witchcraft is my aim—my mind is set on malice,
So I am here to place a curse upon the Royal Palace.
The Royal Queen must be dethroned, also her Kingly Master,
And I shall work with all my will to bring them to disaster.

This was followed by the entry of the fairies:

>Here we come wishing you joy today,
>>Joy today,
>>Joy today,
>May all your future be bright and gay
>In spite of the Sister's warning.

Thereafter the story followed the traditional Cinderella one more or less accurately to the end, when Prince Charming, babbling the third line so as to get all the words safely in, told the Ugly Sisters:

>I want you girls to understand
>I'm just a friendly fella
>I only fought with you to win the hand
>Of lovely Cinderella. . . .

A Harlequinade followed.

Gladys, Benny, Lily and the fairies (twelve of them) roomed in a house that overlooked twenty-two pairs of railroad tracks on which most of the work was done at night. Engines shunted there from midnight until dawn. Metal clanged, whistles blew, jets of steam shot angrily into the air immediately outside the Buckells' bedroom window. It was hardly surprising that Benny slept badly, or that the fairies, most of whom had gone to bed hungry in the first place, wept into their pillows. (During the Christmas pantomime season, children are allowed to work on the stage if they are properly supervised. The Wombshaw pantomime fairies—they were professionally known as Jaywick's Juveniles—hailed from the Glasgow slums, and they were supervised personally by Mrs. Jaywick, who was responsible for their engagement, training and cut-rate living arrangements.)

Benny disliked pantomime at the best of times, and he found Wombshaw one of the worst he had struck. Lack of sleep made him irritable, and it did not improve his temper to find that however great the racket in the marshaling yards, both his wife and his sister-in-law slept perfectly. Benny's nights were poor and his days were not much better. The Buckells' room was small, and for the first few weeks of the show Gladys kept it partly submerged in insertion elastic. She did not sew either well or fast and she had a great deal of sewing to do, for the clothes that Alf Hall had issued to her were the ones made for last year's Ugly Sister, when the part had been played by a tall, rawboned, female impersonator.

Gladys and Benny had their first quarrels—a series of them—during the run of the Wombshaw pantomime. Benny found fault with Gladys' work, accusing her of making mistakes in their routines and ignoring his instructions. He shouted at his wife and his wife shouted back at him, and then Benny would either slam out of the house, or sit in a corner sulking. He took their quarrels seriously. Gladys did not take them seriously enough. It did not occur to her that a marriage might be menaced by a wife's argumentativeness, or that a man would rather have his shortcomings noticed and fussed over than laughed at or ignored. The situation was not improved by the arrival in the town of a whole succession of talent scouts—Wombshaw pantomime was considered a fine shopwindow —who thought no more highly of Cinderella's Ugly Sisters than they had of the Variety Three.

When the pantomime season ended, Gladys and Benny returned

to The Nag's Head, where, under the soothing influence of quiet nights, good cooking and Holly's admiration, Benny's temper improved. He apologized to Gladys for his behavior. "Janey used to say my ambition would ruin me," he said. "I expect you've been thinking the same thing."

"How could I," Gladys said, "when I'm ambitious myself?"

Benny looked shrewdly at her. "You are? You've never seemed so. Since when?"

Gladys hesitated. "All my life, I think. More than anything in the world, I want to be good—*really* good."

Benny laughed. "Darling! I don't know when I've heard anything so absurd. You *are* good—already you are. You must believe that. I know I've said a lot of things lately to make you think otherwise, but that's only because I want you to be more than good—you're capable of the best. We mustn't hurry things, but the time will come. You'll see."

"Benny—"

He had misunderstood her, but she didn't try to explain. Communicating wasn't easy for either of them. If they failed, as they usually did, to find the right words with which to express their thoughts—stabbing uneasily about, like people trying to spear olives with blunt forks—they gave up. With so much in each other that each could enjoy, what was the sense in bothering with areas where neither felt comfortable or at home?

5

BENNY had said they mustn't hurry, and he meant it. All the same, a couple of years in the concert party world was the most that he had envisaged, and when, in 1922, the Variety Three was still traveling the northern circuits, he grew anxious, haunted by the thought that history might be repeating itself.

By the summer of 1922, only Edith was living at home. At Skunby-on-Sea, Blanche stage-managed the Larks, and Flo danced with them. Across England, in one of three pierrot shows playing Assheton Sands, a city of a hundred thousand on the Lancashire coast, Gladys and Benny and Lily were members of the Highlights, a pierrot troupe owned by Chip Lansbury, Joe's youngest brother.

The company at Assheton was not a socially distinguished one, but Lily's presence almost made it seem so. The summer before, Lily had married Jamie Leake—in Skunby Church, and in a hurry between daytime shows. The young couple had been considerate enough to break the news to the Dowager Lady Leake (as Lady Leake became as soon as Jamie married) after the wedding had taken place, thus giving Elizabeth Leake the opportunity to behave correctly, and receive Lily not as the barmaid she thought her, but as the daughter-in-law she was. The Dowager did not fail. She at once treated Lily with kindness and generosity. Massive pieces of coarsely set family jewelry were immediately presented, and discussions set afoot concerning the rooms that would now be turned into the Dowager's private apartments. Jamie and his bride, in spite of the fact that they could not afford it, intended to make Leake Revel their home.

In the opinion of Martin Hay, Jamie Leake had done very well for himself. There was little chance, with the health he had, that he would ever be able to earn a living, and although some wives would have looked upon this as a drawback in a husband, Lily did not. All her life she had been enamored of the Leake family and their great crumbling house: the stone and iron lettering that spelled *Officio Fungi* so frequently about the place would never gather moss while Lily was Leake Revel's chatelaine. All she asked was to be allowed, in so far as she could, to be the family breadwinner, a request that, since Jamie considered his wife's talents only exceeded by her grace and charm, was immediately approved.

Flo had made progress too. At the age of fourteen she had already received more publicity than the rest of her sisters put together. Not only had she won Skunby's "Prettiest Girl in Town" competition, but also she was picked (by a London tabloid) as the most promising dancer appearing anywhere on the 1922 pierrot stage.

Fred and Holly were consumed with astonishment at their children's achievements. Fred could not think how he had come to father three actresses, to say nothing of a titled lady and a highly valued stage manager. Edith was much more the kind of daughter he had expected to find in the family—a gentle, quiet girl, not at all clever.

Edith had now been out of school two years. She worked at The

Nag's Head—she really *was* a barmaid. Her friends in the village teased her for being the only non-pierrot among the sisters, but Edith had no wish to act, although she liked to hear about it.

Gladys wrote from Assheton Sands:

DEAR EDITH,

After Chip Lansbury the Variety Three's got top billing here what do you think of that. There's a nice fellow in the Co with us think you would like him name Tom Holt sings bass. His folks are Grand Opera which he doesn't sing good enough to be but I tell him it's Grand Opera's loss. Tom was born on a stage can you believe it not even a dressing room though they did get the curtain down in time he says.

Tell Flo next time she run short of white ruffs use a pie frill they hold up lovely two hours.

Lovingly,

GLAD

6

THE Highlights' theater at Assheton Sands was larger than the pier theater at Skunby, and the Variety Three had to alter its style somewhat to fit the bigger house. The change was, however, an improvement, and in Benny's opinion, although the act could have done with stronger support than Lily could provide, it was as good now as he could hope to make it with the present cast. In view of this, Benny decided that, at the end of the Highlights' present season, he and the two sisters must make the break he had been talking about for so long.

Two courses lay open to him. Either he could take the act south and look for work in London, or he could form a concert party on his own.

Since none of the talent scouts from the national theatrical agencies who had seen the Variety Three so far had thought favorably enough of them to offer the three artistes a contract, it was unlikely that they would have much luck in London. On the other hand, the formation of a new concert party meant breaking into circuits that already had plenty of established concert parties to choose from—the wartime shortage of entertainers had been over for some while. Establishing contacts took time, even for actors known, as Benny and the Millers were, to many of the provincial theater managers, and time was short; Benny had already spent most of the summer trying to make up his mind what to do.

Lily was eager for them to go to London. She felt convinced that with Benny's stage connections and her own social ones a West End engagement would easily be forthcoming. Gladys did not care what they did. She was perfectly willing for them to go on as they were, adding new songs and sketches to the act from time to time and touring with it year after year, either in one of the Lansbury family concert parties or some other.

And then, on the first of September, a week before the pier theater at Assheton was scheduled to close, and when the Variety Three still had no winter plans made, the ideal job fell into Benny's lap. It arrived in the form of a telegram, which Benny read alone at the Buckells' boardinghouse—Gladys had stayed behind at the theater after the 3:30 show to mend a couple of torn costumes.

The telegram was from Joe Lansbury. It said at some length that with the end of the present season, Joe was giving up the Lansbury Larks. He had consulted the other members of his family and agreed with them to offer Benny and Gladys first refusal of the company's good will (tabs, props, costumes, etc.) as well as the following summer's work on Skunby pier. Joe added that if the Buckells were interested, he was sure that they could come to satisfactory terms.

7

THE sewing took Gladys longer than she had expected. The light in the women's dressing room was poor (it was a naked gas flame) and she did not possess a thimble. Through a small window set high in the dressing-room wall, she could hear the wind and the gulls and the breaking waves, and occasionally, on a gust of wind, the sound of the calliope music from the fun fair. She had mended a tear in her pierrot jacket and was reaching for an evening gown, one shoulder strap of which was held in place by a safety pin that

Part IV

had already ripped a hole, when she heard *The Manxman's* siren. *The Manxman* was a pleasure steamer which came to Assheton Sands every Saturday from Douglas, Isle of Man. *The Manxman* moored at the pier head just above the Highlights' theater and she was now, at half-past five, ready to take her passengers on board again for the trip home. Gladys tried to hurry. She had a twenty-minute walk home to high tea, and Benny as well as the landlady would fuss if she were late.

By the time she had finished her sewing, Gladys could hear footsteps hurrying up the pier. *The Manxman's* passengers always stayed in Assheton as long as they dared—every week there was the same last-minute scramble to the boat. As Gladys came out of the stage door, she met Tom Holt, the Highlights' bass, coming in. She made a face at him. "I stayed too long sewing," she said. "I forgot this was a *Manxman* day."

"I'll come down to the pier gates with you," Tom said. "It'll be easier for two of us to make way against the crowd."

Gladys objected, but Tom took her arm and as he had said they made much better progress together than Gladys would have managed alone. The visitors from the island seemed to fill the pier. Fathers, their arms full of packages and raincoats, led the way, mothers followed, shouting at children who dragged behind. It was an orderly crowd, orderly, that is, until quite suddenly its steady forward movement fell apart. Tom, who wore spectacles when he was not on the stage and who could not see very well even with them on, did not at first understand the reason for the confusion. He felt Gladys wrench her arm free and saw her run. He followed.

A little boy had fallen off the pier into the sea. Most of the pier was enclosed by a wooden guard rail, but there was one place where a flight of steps led down to some boat moorings, and here, across the top of the steps, there was only a short length of chain. It all happened very quickly, and yet by the time Gladys had climbed down to the boat moorings, the little boy was already partly submerged. He lay face down with his head and shoulders below the surface of the choppy water, and his khaki-colored shorts (they looked like an inflated brown paper bag) above.

Gladys kicked off her shoes and jumped, landing in the water close beside the boy. She could not swim, but fortunately Tom knew this and, divesting himself as rapidly as he could of everything but his underdrawers and socks, he dived in after her. He made first for the child, grabbing him and heaving him up on to the mooring platform. Then he pulled Gladys out. She was spluttering and choking and thrashing wildly. By the time he had everybody rescued several men with life jackets and ropes had appeared on the platform, and an ambulance was being driven up the pier. The crowd (*The Manxman* forgotten) was hanging over the railing, shouting and cheering. Tom Holt, still a pierrot in spite of his lack of almost any costume at all, could not let this opportunity pass. "Don't forget the Highlights!" he shouted back. "Three shows every weekday!"

* * *

Benny was so pleased with Joe's telegram that he couldn't wait for Gladys to come home to tea. He hurried down to the theater to meet her, thinking that they would celebrate by having a meal downtown. As he approached the pier, the big gates opened and an ambulance drove out. It contained, although Benny did not find this out until a few minutes later, his wife, Tom Holt, the small boy who had caused all the trouble and the small boy's father. The pier master was taking no chances.

8

THE coast at Assheton Sands is not safe for swimming, even for people who swim well. Although the sands themselves run smooth, level and golden for many miles, the sea is full of ground swells and unpredictable currents that regularly, in spite of warning notices, take their toll of holiday-makers. Gladys had been mad to leap into the sea in the way she did, though Assheton did not look upon her behavior as mad. The little boy she had tried to rescue was an Assheton child, the son of one of the lodginghouse keepers— he had gone to the pier with his father to see an uncle off by the Douglas boat. It was the child's father that the town considered mad for letting the little boy out of his sight. Gladys was a heroine.

Tom Holt's part in the adventure was overlooked by everyone in Assheton except the parents of the boy and the Variety Three:

they never forgot it. The public fuss—and there was plenty—was all directed at Gladys. An hour before the Highlights' curtain time, every inch of space in their theater was filled. A basket of flowers with the pier master's card in it awaited Gladys at the stage door.

Gladys herself nearly missed the show. If the doctor on casualty duty at the hospital had had his way, she would have stayed there overnight, for she had swallowed a great deal of salt water and she was shaken as well as sick. But the doctor was not a pierrot fan (like many of Assheton's permanent residents, he had not been near the sea front for years) and he had no idea who she was. When the odd-looking sextet (Benny, Chip Lansbury, Lily and Jamie Leake followed Tom and Gladys as soon as they heard what happened) promised him that Gladys would go straight to bed the moment she got back to her rooming house, and remain there in perfect quiet until the following afternoon, the doctor gave the patient an envelope of sleeping pills and let her go.

Perfect quiet! The Highlights' eight o'clock show was the noisiest the company had enjoyed all summer. Whenever Gladys appeared, the audience whistled and shouted and stamped. The story of the rescue—considerably embellished by now—was all over town.

It should have been one of the great evenings of Gladys' life, but in fact it was a nightmare. Chip Lansbury set an old tin bucket in the wings, and Gladys availed herself of this consideration every time she came off the stage. During the intermission (the Highlights had a twenty-minute break halfway through the show) some newspapermen came backstage and insisted on taking pictures. Gladys clung to Benny and tried to smile, but her head reeled and her stomach felt as if at any moment it would leave her body altogether and fly away. When the newsmen left, she collapsed, sobbing and saying that she could not go on.

Benny took her outside, where it was dark and cold. There was no one about. Holding her close, he told her about Joe Lansbury's telegram—this was the first chance he had had. "Joe feels about your work just the way I do," he said. "He knows that his show, *any* show, is all right if it's in your hands."

He supposed that she would think from this remark that he was concerned about the Lansbury Larks, when really what was on his mind was the Highlights. He had exactly ten minutes in which to calm his wife and get her changed and back on the stage.

Gladys understood what he was after and, although she would have liked to resist, she felt too wretched to make the effort. She remembered the time Martin Hay had been determined to send her onto a stage when she hadn't wanted to go there—arguing hadn't helped then—it wouldn't now. Without saying anything, Gladys moved out of Benny's arms. Finding that she could stand without his support (she had not been sure of this) she turned and went back into the theater. Shortly afterward, the whole house was singing with her.

Benny breathed a sigh of relief. From the way Gladys looked now, nobody would know that there'd been anything wrong.

9

WITH the help of the doctor's pills, Gladys slept well that night. When she awoke it was nearly noon—and Sunday, with the next pierrot show twenty-three hours away. Benny had gone out. Gladys dozed, feeling very comfortable and warm, although her legs ached. Down the street someone hammered with even, methodical strokes, and below, in the rooming-house yard, a pump dripped. The Buckells, as usual, were staying in the unfashionable quarter of the town. Even in their bedroom the air was redolent of fish.

Presently, Benny came back. He had shaved and he looked very neat and tidy. He was carrying a tray with tea and toast on it, and he had a couple of newspapers under his arm. Gladys sat up. "Oh, Benny, how did you manage it? I thought we weren't allowed to have meals in our rooms."

"We're not, but after yesterday the landladies in this town consider you above rules." He set the tray down. "Darling, how do you feel?"

"Perfect, except that I seem to ache all over."

"This'll put that right." Benny poured her tea. "And if it doesn't, perhaps those will." He dropped the newspapers on the bed.

"What they say?"

"Quite a lot about you, though one reporter has the bad taste to mention Tom."

Gladys sipped her tea. "I'm sorry, Benny."

Benny did not answer at once. Then he said: "What *were* you thinking of, Glad? We don't need that kind of publicity for the act."

Gladys stared. "Publicity for the act? You don't think I jumped in the sea so as to get my name in the papers?"

"I don't know why you jumped in the sea. You can't have imagined you could save the kid. You know as well as I do that you can't swim."

"I forgot."

"*Forgot* you couldn't swim?"

Gladys nodded.

"There were a couple of other things you forgot," Benny went on. "One is that you could very easily have been drowned, and the other is that I love you."

He had thought that she would open her arms to him then, but she did not move.

"Benny, I got something to say."

"Yes?"

"It's been on my mind some time—I even dreamed about it." She paused. "I'm not meaning to be lazy or ungrateful or anything, but I got to give up. I got to give up the stage."

Benny sat down on the bed. Gladys must be sicker than he thought. Making his voice sound as soothing as he could, he said: "Darling—you had a terrible day yesterday. Perhaps we all did. Let's not discuss anything until you're rested."

"No!" Gladys caught his arm. "No—restin' ain't goin' to make no difference." She searched for words. "Ever since we bin married, I bin working for some boss or other—Joe Lansbury, or Arthur, or one of the others. I want to stop. I want my own home—when'll I ever learn to keep house proper, if I got to work all the time? It's *time* we had our own house, Benny. And a family inside it."

Tread cautiously, Benny thought. Watch your step. You know how she is once she makes up her mind—she doesn't change it. He waited for her to go on, but she didn't seem to have anything more to say. She lay back in the bed in silence, and Benny sat beside her.

Suddenly he understood what she had meant when she said she wanted to be good. She hadn't been referring to professional talent. What was on her mind was something much more simple—the right of every woman to live in obscurity and succeed there, running a man's home, raising his children—unknown except to a small circle of relatives and neighbors living equally obscurely. The fact that Gladys had the capacity to live in a world few women can do more than dream about meant nothing to her. And, ironically, he, Benny Buckell, was the reason!

As he so often did when he was baffled, Benny took refuge in anger. The trouble with women like Gladys, he thought, is that because they're strong, they have no sympathy for weakness. They're gay and courageous and passionate and loyal—they're always the conquerors. They don't know what fear is (when she jumped into the sea, she didn't even remember that she couldn't swim) and they don't know what it means to face a situation that's too big for them, or to go through life nagged by an idea. Gladys would give her life for me at any time, but if I ask her to give up this nonentity she's craving for, she'll refuse. She'll say that her professional success will only interfere with our happiness, and arguing with her will be like fighting a waterfall.

In reality, however, the truth of the situation was neither as dark nor as noble as Benny pictured it. While he sat scowling over the saintliness of his wife's character, Gladys wrapped his hopes up in the morning newspaper and handed them back to him, scarcely tarnished at all by the separation. Turning over the pages of the *Assheton Sunday Star*, she exclaimed: "We must send a telegram to The Nag's Head! Mum'll have a fit if she sees these pictures. You know how she fusses about us girls when we're not together."

A tiny light glimmered on Benny's horizon. He nodded. "I'll send one to Joe too while I'm about it," he said. "If we're quite sure we don't want to accept his offer." He turned Gladys' face to his. "Dearest, that was wonderful what you said just now. You must love me."

"I do. You know I do. . . ."

A while later, Benny said: "I was thinking—if you feel that you *would* like to do one season at Skunby (we needn't contract for more than next summer) it'd be our job to cast the show, so we could take on all you girls together for once—even find something for Edith behind the scenes if she'd come. Then at least there'd be one season when your mother'd see the whole family at work on one job. I should love to see her face."

It was a chance shot, and it worked. Gladys' eyes shone. "D'you know," she said, "that never even *occurred* to me? And it won't only be Mum's face you'll love to see—it'll be mine too. I think perhaps I'm just as happy as she is when we're all together."

Keep her hand to the plow a little longer, he thought, and the opportunity to look back may never come again. His blood raced. He hadn't thought for a moment he could manage her as easily as that.

Part V

1

WHEN Mrs. Pegler heard about the formation of the Glad Rags—as Benny called the new pierrot company—she wrote to Gladys suggesting that the Buckells rent Buena Vista. Gladys knew the place. It was a roomy, Victorian mansion, built in ornate, English-seaside style (red brick with turrets, high ceilings, cupolas and a sprawling veranda), that stood on the far side of Skunby's fun fair, about a mile from the center of town. Its name seemed to be based on the fact that the view, except at high tide, was of a somber expanse of greenish-black mud. The esplanade ended at the fun fair, and a sign said UNMADE ROAD BEYOND THIS POINT. The unmade road, a sandy lane, led past a row of shacks to Buena Vista, and came to an end beside the stretch of mud. The Peglers had bought the house with the idea of renting it at a high weekly rate to summer tenants, but unfortunately, not long after their purchase was completed, Skunby fun fair was enlarged and the house of fun erected. The occupants of Buena Vista did not mind the routine noises of the fun fair, but the awful laughter of the papier-mâché clown outside the house of fun drove them frantic, and except at Bank Holiday week ends and on other occasions when the town was overcrowded, nobody would stay there.

Mrs. Pegler pointed out that the house would make an ideal home for the Buckells—they would have both space and privacy. Tourists never went beyond the fun fair, and as for the papier-mâché clown, he was not turned on until two in the afternoon, when the pierrots would be at work, and he was turned off at eleven, when they would be at supper. He could not bother them.

The Buckells accepted at once. Buena Vista meant that at long last Gladys would have a home. The privacy that the Peglers had mentioned turned out to be only partial, however, on account of the other Miller sisters. As usual, the girls looked upon the home of any one of them as the home of all. It did not occur to Blanche and Flo to live anywhere else but in Gladys' house if Gladys' house had room, and the Leakes (Lily and Jamie) moved into Buena Vista the same week Gladys and Benny did.

Benny did not object. He understood the Millers well enough by now to know what to expect. The arrangement meant that he could keep his promise to Gladys to provide all the sisters with jobs. Buena Vista had to have a housekeeper, and when Edith heard this, she jumped at the chance to attach herself even to this remote edge of the glamorous pierrot world. Edith did not want to act, and stage-management responsibilities like Blanche's would have terrified her, but when Benny, who insisted on everyone who lived at Buena Vista contributing in some way to the Glad Rags show, asked her to become wardrobe mistress as well as housekeeper, she jumped at that too. Edith sewed well, and liked it. Jamie Leake was given a more exposed job—he was the company's barker. Half an hour before the curtain time of each performance, Jamie was to take up a position at the pier gates, armed with a megaphone. Jamie had never done anything of the kind before, and he looked forward to opening day with trepidation.

Benny persuaded the town council to buy a new piano. It was a grand, and the stage had to be extended beyond the proscenium arch to accommodate it. This meant that the view from the front seats was a steep one, but Benny assured the council that they would be the most sought after in the house, and this proved to be true. Benny also bought new curtains. They were white, with a gay design of red gladioli climbing up them. There were new pierrot costumes too—white and red, to match the curtains, instead of the traditional white and black.

Opening day, as usual, was Whitmonday. Jamie Leake thought his barking must have been effective: there was a good house. As the gladioli curtains were pulled aside, the artistes lined up along the footlights and sang:

> The seaside is famed for its fine sun and air
> The sun and the air are so bracing
> The sun may be fine, but for that I don't pine
> It's the daughters I find most embracing,
> You can have all the ozone, by Gad!
> But give me a flapper and I'm some bad lad. . . .

This was just the kind of thing the audience was hoping for, and they gave the Glad Rags a tremendous hand.

2

SKUNBY soon became devoted to the Glad Rags. Oddly enough, Jamie seemed to take to his new job like a nervous duck to a strange pond, objecting volubly to begin with, and then becoming self-important. He bought himself a scarlet blazer and a monocle, and after that he hardly needed the megaphone—people stopped to listen to him anyway. The only time Jamie allowed anybody else to bark for him was when the Dowager Lady Leake came to town. All the Glad Rags felt that there was a limit to which even *Officio Fungi* could be asked to go.

It was fortunate that there was so much space at Buena Vista, for it was not long before Tom Holt also moved there. Tom was one of those courteous and considerate persons who are irresistibly drawn to brutal landladies. However careful Tom was about selecting a place to stay, the one he finally settled on was always miserable. On one occasion the extreme age and frailty of the lady he agreed to board with seemed to bode at least a modicum of peace, but Tom had no chance to find out because the lady died on opening night. Theatrical lodgings in seaside towns are apt to be less comfortable than those inland because an actor who remains all summer does not pay as much as the tourist who is replaced by another tourist each Saturday morning. Tom understood this and he willingly changed his room to suit the convenience of more free-spending customers. One week he would roast in the attic, the next, freeze in the cellar. Never, therefore, until he came to Skunby with the Glad Rags, had he been thrown out into the street.

The occasion was his birthday. Tom, who was in the attic that week, invited the company to come around to his lodgings and celebrate. His birthday fell on a Sunday, so the party was arranged for early evening, when the landlady was at church. For some reason, before the beer was opened or the food touched, the landlady came home. Accusing Tom of holding an orgy in her absence on the Sabbath day, she ordered everyone to leave. The Glad Rags obeyed, deftly sweeping food, drink and Tom's small wardrobe into their arms as they did so. It was a simple matter to transfer the party to Buena Vista in a taxi (the beer bottles, sardine-stuffed buns, underwear, shoes, and chicken-spread crackers heaped together on the floor), but when the party was over Tom had no place to go home.

It was actually Edith, and not the Buckells, who invited Tom to stay. Edith had admired Tom ever since she had sent him his first and only piece of fan mail. It was dated September 5, 1922, and read:

DEAR MR. HOLT,

I know you will have had many congratulations on your great feat of daring in rescuing the little boy and my sister from certain death but I hope you will permit me to say that in my opinion only a man of Noble Character would act in such a way without a thought to his own conveniences.

Pardon my liberty in writing but I felt I simply got to.

Yours faithfully,

EDITH MILLER

Tom had carried the letter in his wallet ever since.

Edith's style of cooking and housekeeping was just right for Buena Vista. The large, heavy meals she prepared could be eaten equally well at any time. They were the kind that taste much the same whether freshly made or warmed over. On Sundays, breakfast often lasted until lunch began, and lunch might stretch on until those who had eaten early were ready to eat again; the same big pot of tea, rejuvenated at intervals with boiling water and a scattering of fresh leaves, doing duty without interruption throughout the day. Housecleaning was of the haphazard, or Nag's Head, sort —Edith did not let her many tasks become a burden.

In the hubbub at Buena Vista, Tom Holt would probably have been no more comfortable than he had been with his previous landladies had it not been for Edith. She fussed over him as no one had ever done before. Their romance, for that is what it came to, developed slowly. In 1923 it was no more than a wistful thought in Edith Miller's mind.

Looking at the crowd of people he appeared to have married, Benny wondered sometimes why Cookie did not move into Buena

Vista too. Cookie, however, had no need. His experience with landladies was the exact opposite of Tom's. Wherever Cookie lived, he was treated as if he were the overindulged only son of the house. Usually he would occupy the best bedroom, always he enjoyed the largest helpings at meals, and when he returned home after the evening show, he would find some small savory-smelling offering left simmering on the back of the stove.

But Cookie might not have moved to Buena Vista in any case. His feeling for Gladys had never changed, and since he had to work with her, he didn't want to live in the same house with her as well. Cookie was faithful, devoted, and clever enough not to be persistent. Gladys was very fond of him.

After the one explosion in the bedroom at Assheton Sands, Gladys had said nothing more about exchanging the stage for housework, but she had not forgotten about it. Benny hadn't forgotten either, however, and he gave much thought to contriving lures to keep his wife in the show. He made it clear to Gladys that he was staking everything on her. He put the little money he had saved into the new company, and when this was insufficient for all he wanted to do, he persuaded Joe Lansbury to leave in the Glad Rags most of what was due to him for the Larks' good will. It was Benny who bought the gladioli curtains and the pierrots' new clothes. By Miller standards, a lot of money was involved. Then there was the company's name. The Glad Rags pierrot show, with curtains with gladioli on them and costumes to match, made sense only if Glad was in the cast.

Benny's standards were another lure. He was not easy to please. Gladys found it extremely difficult to extract praise from him, and it was not lost on Benny Buckell that as long as her job was a challenge to her, Gladys would not be willing to give it up.

Benny also saw to it that the pleasures of a star's life were not neglected. The Glad Rags' program was built around Gladys— everybody else in the company, including Benny himself, occupied supporting roles. People pointed her out to each other in the street, and ran after her with their cameras. Gladys would hardly have been human if she had not enjoyed the fuss they made.

But the strongest of all Benny's lures was the Miller sisters. They loved their connection with the Glad Rags, and they worked splendidly together.

By fall, when the pier theater closed for the winter, Gladys found herself, as Benny had hoped she would, too deeply committed to leave. So she went out with the Glad Rags concert party on their winter tour, and the following summer, for a variety of reasons, she returned with them to Skunby.

Gladys was not sufficiently analytical to realize what was going on. All she understood was that if she wished to maintain her sisters' happiness and her husband's fortunes, she must stay where she was, at any rate for the present. Her intention to give up her work, genuine though it was, became, therefore, something to be done *soon*, rather than *now*, and as is so often the case, *soon* almost immediately began to fade in the strong light of *now*.

Benny was careful. When Gladys questioned him about the Glad Rags' future, he was always scrupulously vague. He pointed out that there was no reason to suppose that the company's present popularity would continue indefinitely—every troupe expected bad years along with the good. This satisfied Gladys. When we stop doing so well, she thought, then it will be all right for me to give up. Or I may have a baby.

Neither of these eventualities occurred. There was no baby, and the Glad Rags, if anything, increased in favor.

3

GAILY colored posters all over Skunby-on-Sea welcomed the summer's visitors:

Skunby-on-Sea
Welcomes You in 1925!
Don't Miss
The Illuminations—
The Girl Entombed Alive in Ice—
The Smallest Married Couple—
and
Every Weekday on the Pier
At 11, 3, and 8
THE GLAD RAGS
Your Favorite Pierrots

Across the front of the pier theater, visible far down the esplanade, the name GLAD RAGS flashed on and off all evening in garish yellow lights. There had been some other changes too since Joe Lansbury's time. Aside from the new piano and the enlarged stage it necessitated, a cold-water faucet had been installed in the passageway between the stage and the dressing rooms, and the lighting system had been completely overhauled. This was the company's third season in Skunby, and business was booming. They were the biggest attraction in the town.

Gladys had now had nearly seven years' experience in the pierrot and concert party world, and in this minor firmament she had become a star. She was heavier than she had been, which improved her looks without making her any less light on her feet, and her voice was superb, whether used at its purest for "Ave Maria," or with a screech in it for:

> Don't swat yer mother, boys, just 'cause she's old!
> Don't mop the floor with her face.
> Think how her love is a treasure of gold,
> Shining through shame and disgrace.
> Don't put the rocking chair next to her eye,
> Don't bounce the lamp off her bean!
> Angels are watching you up in the sky,
> Don't swat yer mother, it's mean!

The Glad Rags company this year consisted of Gladys, Benny, Flo, Tom Holt, Lily, Cookie and Billie Whittington, the girl contortionist from Gladys' Merry Men days. In addition, Benny engaged guest artistes for a week or so at a time—a conjuror, a man with a troupe of performing poodles, another man who had a clever, evil-smelling seal. Cookie and the grand piano provided the accompaniment. One of the advantages of the new instrument from Cookie's point of view was that it was now possible for the orchestra to keep a hot cup of tea beside him while he worked: nobody could see it, set on the strings inside the lid.

Blanche stage-managed the show, and most of the company's problems were solved by hollering for her and leaving the current difficulty, whatever it might be, in her capable hands. Her resources, like her religious convictions, seemed unfailing. The same thing, to a lesser degree, might have been said of the wardrobe mistress, Edith.

Although the Glad Rags were so popular with Skunby audiences, Joe Lansbury was not forgotten. Whenever he visited the pier theater—at least once a week during the season—Gladys made him come up on the stage and take a bow. Joe loved this—he found leisure a greatly overrated commodity. Since his retirement, he had had a series of operations, and now he was never really well. But even this, he confided to Gladys, had its bright side. His recent internal problems had put Mae way ahead of all her friends in party conversation.

One of the reasons why Joe felt particularly at home when he visited the pier theater was that although the pierrots there had a new name and new clothes, their programs were much the same as the Lansbury Larks', whether one listened to the popular songs:

> Poor little Nellie oft sighs in her sleep
> "Why did they dig Ma's grave so deep?"

or watched the sketches, some of which were so short that they were little more than remarks. The "Maternity Hospital Waiting Room," for instance, consisted merely of:

GLADYS: Congratulations, Mr. Brown! I am delighted to tell you that your wife has triplets.
BENNY: *Triplets*, nurse?
GLADYS: Three beautiful little girls.
BENNY: Well, I never!
GLADYS: You must have!

Gladys and Benny had discontinued the Variety Three. Benny would have liked to make further changes in the show and gradually turn the Glad Rags into a revue, a more stylish form of entertainment, but he had enough sense to realize that his public wanted only what it was accustomed to.

Among the Glad Rags' staple items was a turn, or series of turns, called "Old Time Music Hall." For this, Benny, wearing sideburns and a cutaway coat (the number always appeared in the second half of the program after the Glad Rags had changed out of their pierrot costumes) sat at a small table at the side of the stage upon which were set a tankard of beer and a chairman's gavel. Hammering on the table, Benny would call for silence, so that he could announce the artiste who would sing the next song: "Ladies and Gentlemen, I have much pleasure in presenting to you this evening a celebrated singer who has been brought to Skunby-on-Sea at *enormous* expense *especially* to entertain you"—the audience soon learned this phrase and would join in: "*Enormous* expense!" "*Especially* to entertain you!"—"And here she is—" the chairman would continue, "your own—come on, everybody!—your own, your very own, THE ONE AND ONLY—GLADYS—MILLER!"

While the audience stamped and yelled, Gladys, in a blond wig, would make her entrance, and Cookie would pound out the introductory bars of an old song conveniently adaptable to its present locale:

There was once a simple maiden came to Skunby on a trip
And her golden hair was hanging down her back.
Her cheeks were like the roses, she'd a pout upon her lip,
And her golden hair was hanging down her back.
When she landed at the station here she took a little stroll,
At everything she wondered till she lost her self-control,
Said she "Skunby's quite a village, ain't it? Bless my soul!"
And her golden hair was hanging down her back.

But oh, Jane doesn't look the same,
When she left the village she was shy;
But alas and alack! She's gone back,
With a naughty little twinkle in her eye. . . .

Between songs, Benny would call for the potman. Dressed in a gray derby, a butcher's apron and sideburns as handsome as Benny's own, one of Blanche's stage-struck assistants would hurry onto the stage and remove the chairman's empty glass tankard. In a few moments he would return with it filled. The potman's part was ardently competed for among the local boys, for this was their one chance to be seen. The potman was always the first of the Glad Rags to put on his make-up on Music Hall nights, and the last and most reluctant to remove it. Skunby audiences never failed to give the potman a cheer, nor to be impressed by the number of pints Benny could down in an evening. They suspected that there must be a trick to it somewhere, but none of them ever quite figured out what it was.

In spite of the old songs, the old sketches and the old jokes ("My friend married a pensive little thing. Now he finds she's an ex-pensive little thing.") it was impossible to keep originality wholly away with Gladys and Flo Miller in the cast: their freshness always delighted their audiences. Because of her looks and her talent, Benny did not trust Flo. She would marry soon, and when that happened, being a Miller, all she would want to do would be to give up her stage career.

Benny was only partly right. Flo married soon, but she did not give up her work. Her husband, Billy Dyer, was a second assistant film director, and Flo met him within a week of the pier theater's closing for the winter months, when, in a competition organized by *The Dancing Times*, she won a day's work in a movie.

The Dyer wedding took place in Tor early in October, with Edith and Blanche as bridesmaids and Gladys and Lily as matrons of honor. The Millers did not rent a marquee or hire Mr. Worboys' gold-painted chairs, but Flo's wedding, Gladys thought, was even more beautiful than Margaret Leake's had been. The church bells rang a wedding peal, the choir and the glee club sang, and Flo, her lovely face stricken with happiness, wore Holly's wedding gown.

Benny was not impressed. "Dyer's never going to make any money," he told his wife.

Gladys was shocked. "What an idea, Benny! Flo didn't marry him for money."

Benny shrugged. "Why should she? Flo must know by now that she and her husband, and any children they may have, can always share ours."

"Of course she knows *that*," Gladys replied.

Fred Miller, however, was extremely pleased with his new son-in-law. This time there was neither a mustache nor a title for him to stomach. Billy was a farmer's son, respectable, slightly paunchy and twenty-three. He was in the film industry because the studio where he worked—it was a few miles north of London—had been built on his father's land and stood conveniently across the road from his home.

For Holly, Flo's wedding was neither the anxiety she had anticipated nor the pleasure she had hoped. She would have liked several months in which to arrange everything, but since the war it seemed that even brides were in a hurry. Flo and Billy had a two-day honeymoon, after which Billy returned to his studio, and Flo joined the Glad Rags' autumn tour.

"It don't seem proper to me," Holly grumbled to Fred. "Them goin' their separate ways so soon."

"They're all right," Fred said. "Billy's a good boy."

Holly thought so too, though the same idea had occurred to her that had occurred earlier to Benny. "He don't seem to have much in the way of a *job*, Fred. D'you know what a second assistant director does? He stands beside the Director and shouts '*Quiet*' when the director wants '*Quiet*' shouted! Flo told me."

Fred yawned. The film world was beyond him. "Don't fret, love," he said. "Billy's a good boy."

"Well, he certainly seems devoted to Flo."

"And after so long together, too! You realize they been married all of three days?"

4

GLADYS much preferred the summer work at Skunby to the winter tours, for at Skunby she could live at Buena Vista, and Edith was there. Edith somehow found time to do much more than housekeeping and wardrobe work. If Gladys was tired, Edith brushed her hair for her or massaged her feet. If Gladys took a nap, as she sometimes did between shows, it was Edith who saw to it that no one woke her. But on tour there was no Edith, and no Lily either. Lily's ambitions were equally divided between the Glad Rags and Leake Revel, and during the winter months, Leake Revel won. The old house and the old Dowager both needed her.

The Dowager was aging. She was devoted to her daughter-in-law and no longer thought of her as a barmaid—in fact she had adapted herself with astonishing ease to her close personal connection with The Nag's Head Inn. With Lily in charge of the big house, the Dowager felt free to spend her winters in the way she best liked to spend them, taking long walks over the moors in a balding fur coat that had an inch or two of petticoat showing between it and the tops of her good stout boots.

These were successful years, but for Gladys they were not easy ones. Benny Buckell, for all his experience, was not clever in the way Joe Lansbury had been at keeping his company contented. At Skunby, everything went fairly smoothly, but trouble of one sort or another always seemed to beset the Glad Rags from the moment they took to the road. The long cross-country journeys, which Gladys had enjoyed in the Lansburys' time, now seemed nothing but a succession of cold railway carriages, icy platforms and picnic meals. In Belfast, the company found that there was no boat to the mainland on Sundays, so as soon as the curtain fell on their Saturday night show, the Glad Rags had to run all the way to the quay in costume and make-up, a course of action conducive to short tempers and the leaving of essential belongings behind. Then there were casting difficulties. The Billies, Bobbies and Bubbleses from amongst whom the Glad Rags recruited their successive soubrettes were noisy, quarrelsome, complaining girls who objected, as Gladys remembered Bubbles King had done, to supplying their own fishnet stockings and dancing shoes. Some also resented the billing Benny gave them, others his long rehearsals. Benny alternately flirted and shouted: either way, he found his soubrettes very trying.

The mothers were an even worse problem. Sometimes Benny engaged an additional dancer to supplement or replace Flo, and if the girl was very young, her mother might tour with her. At first the touring mother would make herself useful, taking over the wardrobe duties which at Skunby were so faithfully performed by Edith. Later, as the tour progressed, the mother would become critical and unhelpful. Invariably, they were jealous women, living in their daughters' futures, and by means of a caustic comment here, an unpleasant insinuation there, they were able, with the minimum amount of effort, to create a maximum amount of discord.

Most of the artistes Benny engaged came, like himself, from a theatrical background, but now and again an ambitious debutante would persuade him to take her on. The debutantes were usually singers, and Benny's attitude toward them was ambivalent—he was attracted by their money and their friends, and repelled by their conceit. And a rich girl in the cast invariably meant a row with Gladys, not because Gladys was envious, but because wealth amused her. With the exception of Lily, all the Miller sisters thought it funny to be rich.

But however much she irritated him, and she often irritated him a great deal, Benny never lost sight of the fact that the show depended on Gladys, and that although the Glad Rags was as much her company as his, she must be spared as many of its problems as possible. With Blanche's help, Benny handled the whole of the Glad Rags' finances, and for this Gladys was grateful; she was no better than Holly at handling money. Fortunately, the company's difficulties had no damaging effect on the box office; the Glad Rags were fast becoming as solidly established on the north country circuit as they were at Skunby-on-Sea.

The Miller girls were becoming established too. In 1926, Flo had a son (she named him Launcelot), and the following year, Lily produced a tiny, underweight boy. Young Jamie (no other name for the baby was considered) rejoiced the Dowager to the point of ecstasy, for he came into this drafty world bearing a clearly defined Leake nose.

During these years, London talent scouts visited the show fairly frequently. Benny always tried to impress them by talking importantly about his plans, and by entertaining them as lavishly as the resources of the town the company was in at the time permitted. Gladys thoroughly enjoyed her husband's parties, but she was convinced that the scouts would only be impressed by what they saw on the stage, not by what and where they ate after the show was over. So she behaved very badly. Ignoring Benny's furious signals, she would whistle across a dining room to attract a waiter's attention, or shout and wave if she recognized a friend. This made the scouts laugh, and the waiters. It also insured that the evening would end in the way many evenings did now: in quarreling. Some of these quarrels were made up making love, but this did nothing to strengthen the structure of their relationship. The real privilege of marriage—the right to walk about in the mind of another person as if that garden were your own—was one that neither Benny nor Gladys knew of.

Benny made no effort to explain himself. He sulked. He was still as sure as he had ever been that Gladys belonged at the top of her profession, but none of the scouts seemed to agree with him, and Gladys, so far as he could see, was determined to stay somewhere well below center. Listening as a tired audience in some cold hall filled the place with gale after gale of delighted laughter, or watching their spellbound faces as Gladys sang, Benny would feel enormously proud and sure of her. But then, the next night perhaps, a talent scout would appear in the audience, and nothing whatever would come of his visit except that at supper after the show, Gladys would play the fool and shame him, ruining (or so he felt) all their chances of success with her childish behavior.

It did not occur to Benny that the reason Gladys' behavior was childish was that in many ways she *was* childish. All her life she had matured only by jolts and starts, and always late. At the age of twenty-seven, she had brought the Glad Rags a following in their own part of the country, but there was no knowing whether she would interest London next year, or in five years' time, or not at all. Everything that Benny thought about his wife was correct except the timing—he did not understand that Gladys had to be left alone to grow at her own pace. Not that it would have helped if he had understood, for he would not have had the patience to wait.

There was, however, one man who did. George Garrison, the London producer, was well aware of Gladys Miller, and his scouts were watching her. On one occasion, unknown to the Glad Rags, Garrison himself saw a part of their show, and he had also heard Gladys on the radio—the Glad Rags broadcast sometimes from one of the provincial stations of the B.B.C. George Garrison, unlike Benny Buckell, was in no hurry. He was quite prepared to let Gladys develop in her own good time—and in somebody else's show.

5

IT WAS in 1928 that Gladys finally had to admit to herself that her marriage was breaking up. For some time, in spite of her determined efforts to ignore the problem, she had been becoming more and more aware of it. The break was piecemeal, and expressed in a great many small, pointless quarrels.

It never occurred to Gladys that the fault was largely hers. She loved her husband, but it was an easy, casual love that had no time for Benny's little vanities and snobberies. Matters that were extremely important in his eyes looked petty to Gladys, and she said so. It was a situation that should never have been allowed to wreck a marriage, and if Gladys had been more tactful, or Benny less pompous about himself, it would not; but Gladys teased where she should have used tact, and Benny did not like being laughed at.

Gladys made no effort to salvage her marriage. She had no idea what effort to make. No one had ever explained to her that happy marriages do not simply occur—they are built. In her mind, a broken marriage was like epilepsy or blindness—a tragedy that happened sometimes in other people's families, not in her own. Because she did not know what to do, she behaved in the way Holly always behaved when faced with unpleasantness: she carried on as usual and did her best to pretend that the problem did not exist. Putting a cheerful face on everything, Gladys ignored the danger signs.

In any other world than that of pierrots and concert parties, where private life is so publicly lived, and where the chief relaxation of everyone is a nice cup of tea and a nice slice of gossip to go with it, this might have worked. It didn't work at all with the Glad Rags. Benny, in seeking consolation for his disappointed hopes, turned not to drink, which the company would have resented, nor to indolence, which they would have despised, but to other women, which intrigued them all. The Miller sisters were too loyal to discuss their sister's predicament in public, but no such restraint afflicted the stagehands, guest artistes, dancers, soubrettes and (hardly!) the mothers. To these persons, the real or imagined infidelities of the leading lady's husband made irresistible topics of conversation, particularly when the husband was still an attractive man, and the leading lady seemed to take him very much for granted.

When the Glad Rags were at work, Benny was as attentive to his wife as he had always been, but once a performance or rehearsal was over, he was apt to disappear. Sometimes, Gladys would run into him in the town, out with the soubrette of the moment or one of the dancing girls, and she would smile and wave, as if the situation were perfectly normal and equally agreeable to all of them. Neither she nor Benny would refer to the incident afterward. Other times, Benny's hunger for her persuaded Gladys to think she must have imagined the difficulties between them, but Gladys did not realize that bodily and spiritual union are neither the same thing, nor inseparable.

The sisters offered advice. Blanche wanted a family conference called, at which Benny would be invited to explain himself. A full and frank discussion would settle everything, Blanche thought. Fortunately, everybody else shrank from that. Edith's solution was that since Gladys had no baby of her own, she should adopt one. Benny would settle down once he was given the responsibilities of a father. Flo, who in her time had received a pass or two from her brother-in-law herself, did not feel in a position to comment. She wore that aura of remoteness pregnant women wear—Flo was expecting her second child—and her sister's problems did not at the moment seem important to her. Lily thought everything would be all right if only Gladys would spend more time and money on her clothes, and visit a good hairdresser. Indicating a loose thread hanging from the place on Gladys' blouse where a button should have been, Lily said: "A woman should always be immaculate."

"What a thing to say, Lily!" Blanche exclaimed. "You *know* Glad's a Protestant."

It was Mae Lansbury who brought matters into the open. A few days before the end of the 1928 summer season (Edith's wedding to Tom Holt was to take place in Tor the following Sunday), Gladys sat drinking tea in Mae's shiny little front parlor. Joe was taking a nap, and, surprisingly, Gladys was the only guest. Mae said: "Joe tells me you and Benny's plannin' on takin' Bobbie Brown on the tour this autumn. That's a mistake."

"Why, Mae? Benny's known her for years."

"I'll say!" Mae paused and wheezed a little. "And a lot better than he oughta, if you understand me." She patted Gladys' knee. "You got to keep an eye on that boy of yours, Gladdie. You bin married a while. Show some sense and keep Bobbie out of the show. You know what men are."

But that, of course, was Gladys' trouble. She only knew, and that somewhat vaguely, what Fred was like, and Jamie Leake, and placid little Billy Dyer. None of them were any help. All the same, she decided to follow Mae's advice. That night, when Benny came to bed, Gladys said: "Mae says we shouldn't take Bobbie Brown on the tour because she used to be your girl."

Benny laughed, and said without rancor: "Mae's a bitch."

"Well—was she?"

Benny believed in telling the truth when he could. "Yes," he said, "she was."

I wonder what I say now, Gladys thought. It's no end awkward, talking!

Benny helped her out. He came across the room and gathered her into his arms. "I suppose the next thing you're going to ask is— is she still my girl. Is that it? Listen, Glad. You aren't going to worry your head about every bit of company gossip you hear, are you?"

Gladys clung to him, drowned in relief. "Of course not. It would be silly, wouldn't it, if we couldn't trust each other?"

"Silly as anything," Benny agreed.

6

EDITH and Tom were married in Tor Church on the second Sunday of September, 1928, a week before rehearsals for the Glad Rags' winter tour began. Not all the sisters were able to attend. Flo was at the Dyer home in Hertfordshire with her husband and son, awaiting the arrival of her baby. Lily, with *her* husband and son, was in London, attending the funeral of the Dowager's brother, the old actor, Oliver Marshall. Oliver had died very suddenly, and the Leakes had dashed off, Lily very unhappy at having to choose between her devotion to Edith and her duty to her in-laws.

Edith's wedding day turned out to be one of the most eventful days in the Millers' lives. First there was the ceremony itself. This took place in the morning, after Mattins. The bells rang wedding chimes, the choir sang special music, and Edith wore a white brocade dress that she had made herself in the pier theater wardrobe.

Afterward, when the party was over and the bride and groom had left, a telegram arrived from Billy Dyer, announcing that Flo had a daughter. ("They're goin' to call her Marge," Holly told everyone. "It was Billy's turn to choose. Goes nice with Launcelot, don't it?")

So now more toasts had to be drunk, and it was during this second celebration—it must have been midafternoon by then—that the telephone rang, an event that in itself created a disturbance at The Nag's Head, for the Millers had only recently had a telephone installed. There was even more of a commotion when they discovered it was a long-distance call, from London. Gladys came to the telephone. It was George Garrison's secretary, Miss Wilson. Miss Wilson spoke briefly—she had already spent some time tracing Gladys from Skunby-on-Sea: George Garrison wanted to see Gladys in his London office the next morning, at 11 A.M.

The call could hardly have been better timed. Gladys, although she had been careful not to show it, had been feeling very low all day. The lovely quiet wedding, the fourth wedding now, in the Miller family, and the noisy gathering afterward (beer in the bar for the regular clientele, champagne in the kitchen for the invited few) were wholly spoiled for her by the fact that this was the first time she had come home to The Nag's Head without Benny. Gladys had worried (unnecessarily, as it turned out) over how she should explain Benny's absence to her father. Fred asked, "Where's Benny? He come with you?" but when Gladys replied, "No, he had things at Skunby to see to," Fred, privately relieved, made no further comment.

Gladys had also worried over how she should explain Benny's absence to the village; under normal circumstances Tor enjoyed a good gossip quite as much as the pierrots did. Fortunately this week end the village could think of nothing but Edith and her wedding. Everybody in Tor approved of Tom. The young people were impressed by his grave good looks; the older considered a silent man, who could sing in tune on demand, exactly what a son-in-law should be.

Holly, of course, was not distracted so easily. She learned at once (from Blanche) the real reason why Benny was not at the wedding, and she reacted strongly, in a manner that astonished Gladys. Holly was very fond of Benny Buckell. "Glad," she said to her daughter the first chance they had to be alone, "you know what? Your Benny and his girls is just like my Fred and his rabbits."

"His *rabbits*, Mum?"

"Yes. Fred's rabbits is just something Fred's got to have. Take them away from him, and Fred wouldn't be himself. He needs them the same way I need you children. It took me a while to understand that. Here we would be, half an hour to evening opening time, and the sink still full of the morning's dirty tankards, and where d'you suppose I'd find the innkeeper? Bustling about the bar getting us prepared? Ho no! Out in the yard, as unconcerned as you please, lookin' over his rabbits. It fashed me no end till I got used to it."

"I don't really see, Mum, how—"

"What I mean is, you got to take men the way they are, the bad with the good, and in the long run there's usually a lot more good." Holly hugged her daughter. "Whatever Benny does, just see to it that you have a laugh and a cuddle for him when he wants it."

Miss Wilson's telephone call meant that if Gladys was to be in time for her appointment with Garrison, she must leave Tor that night. There was a nine o'clock train from Manley which, after stopping at every station, reached London in the small hours of the next day. Gladys could go by that, and sleep as best she might during the journey. Holly hastily collected together a basket of food and prepared a thermos of soup. Blanche was concerned about Gladys' clothes. "You know what Lily said about it being important to look tidy," she said. "Let me lend you my best hat. It's big, and it'll absorb your hair, and it's real lucky too—I've had the best times under it."

"Fancy!" Holly exclaimed. "You and Lily in London together, and no way you can get in touch."

Blanche remarked that Lily and Jamie would be back in Tor before she reached Skunby the next afternoon. She added: "What shall I say to Benny when I see him?" Benny would not have known about George Garrison's call. The pier master's office had told Miss Wilson that the Glad Rags were all at The Nag's Head.

"Tell him everything," Gladys said. "And say I'll be on the first train to Skunby I can get after the interview."

In the end she wore a medley of best clothes—a blue silk dress and red wool coat of her own, Blanche's lucky hat (it was black straw, with a wide, floppy brim), a pair of jade earrings belonging to Holly, and Rose Dutton's new white gloves.

Holly and Blanche went to Manley to see Gladys off. Holly worried about the train. "They'll roll milk at every stop, and the noise those cans make! You won't get a wink."

"I'll be all right, Mum. Lordy, I believe I'm *nervous!*"

When they had waved the train out of sight, Blanche said to her mother: "Glad's nervous on account of Benny, but when he hears what's happened, he'll be so proud of her he'll renounce all his wicked ways, you'll see."

Holly wasn't listening. "Oh, Blanche, *look!*" she cried. "I've still got Glad's umbrella. There now! And they say it rains ever so, down there in London."

7

GLADYS reached Euston Station at three A.M. Until seven, she slept on a horsehair sofa in the ladies waiting room, and then, feeling refreshed, she went across the street and ate a large breakfast in a Lyons Tea Shop. When she was excited she was hungry, and she was certainly excited now: this was her first visit to London, and today she would meet George Garrison. Gladys was no more ambitious than she had ever been, but she knew very well how much success meant to Benny, and it would have been impossible for anyone to spend ten years in the pierrot world without absorbing some of the veneration everybody felt for Garrison. "Good enough for a Garrison show"—there was no higher praise than that.

Even after a leisurely meal, Gladys had nearly three hours to spend before her interview. At a kiosk outside the teashop, she bought a street map of London. Garrison's office was in Regent Street, some distance away, but with the help of the map and so much time, she could easily walk there.

It was a beautiful morning, sunny and dry. Euston Road, with its tumble-down shops and little drab hotels, might, Gladys thought, have been the slummy outskirts of any English town except for the scarlet double-decker buses that were rocking along with their loads of early workers. Each bus had a board running the length of it on which advertising matter was displayed. One that Gladys noticed said COMING SOON! A NEW GEORGE GARRISON SHOW.

Gladys walked east a little way, and then south across Cartwright Gardens and down Marchmont Street. She decided from all she saw that she liked London very well. She had expected it to be clean and efficient-looking, but instead it was familiarly gray and dirty, and no one she saw seemed to be in any more of a hurry than she was. Men sat on doorsteps reading newspapers and gossiping, cats wandered about, a coster passed, pushing a barrow loaded with oranges. Gladys met a milkman on his rounds, and a postman. Both smiled at her. Except that the accent of these people was different —sharper, and higher pitched—any of them might just have returned from holidays at Skunby-on-Sea. We'll be all right in London, Gladys thought. It won't be any harder to make the folks here laugh than it is back North.

Her walk took her through several Bloomsbury squares. In Bloomsbury, no one gossiped on doorsteps. There were fewer people about, and more activity. The kitchens of the tall houses lay below the level of the sidewalk and separated from it by an area like a moat, an arrangement that gave Gladys a fine view of maids in blue cotton dresses and white aprons, bustling about getting breakfast. Some of the houses had been turned into offices, and in these the kitchens were mostly dark. Where a light did shine, it revealed the dusty contents of a storeroom.

By the time Gladys reached Oxford Street, she was hungry again. She stopped at the first Lyons Tea Shop she saw and ordered a cup of sweet tea and a bun. She dawdled over the tea, but even so, she reached the Garrison office building nearly an hour too soon. On learning that Garrison occupied the whole of the third floor, she felt hungry again. Fortunately there was another Lyons close by.

This part of London—the crescent of Regent Street—was the London of her imagination: clean, windswept, noisy, and, even at this hour of the morning, colorful and gay. The shops were sparkling with jewelry and women's bright clothes—the wax figures modeling them stared out disdainfully as the tourist from Tor stared in.

Half an hour before the time of her appointment, Gladys stepped into the elevator in the Garrison building. Miss Wilson, a white-haired, middle-aged lady, whose auntly appearance gave no sign of her extreme competence, was accustomed to the eccentric appearance of her employer's callers, but this one, radiant in slept-in finery that did not fit her, exceeded most. Miss Wilson wanted to laugh, but she managed to restrain herself and, smiling warmly instead, she said: "I'm so glad you're early. Mr. Garrison hates to be kept waiting."

George Garrison did laugh. He said: "My God! Take off that frightful hat, and why the coat? Isn't it warm enough in here for you?"

George Garrison was a big man with pale skin, watery blue eyes, and what sounded like taffeta underwear. He liked to walk up and down his large office while he talked, and when he moved, he rustled. This morning he came quickly to the point.

"Sit down. No, over there where I can see you. I've got work for you in my *Big Top Revue*. We go into rehearsal Monday week and open in Manchester November 9. I want to try you out with one number alone and two with the rest of the company."

Gladys said: "Mr. Garrison, I—I—"

"Speak up. No need to be afraid of me."

"I can't come if you're suggesting I come alone. I have my own pierrot show and concert party with my husband, Benny Buckell. My sisters are with us."

George Garrison stopped walking. "Are you telling me you don't want the job?"

Gladys nodded. "Yes. I feel terrible to disappoint you."

"I shall try to get over it."

Garrison tramped off again in the direction of a large desk. When he reached it he swung round and said angrily: "Don't be a fool. I know Benny Buckell. I don't want him, and I don't want your sixteen sisters either. But I've heard you on the radio and I've even sat through parts of your show. You are a clever girl, and this is where you belong."

Gladys' face was scarlet. He is the rudest man I ever met, she thought, and I like him even better than I like Martin Hay.

"I'm not in the habit of begging artistes to work for me," Garrison went on. "And I'm too old to start, but there's something I think you don't understand. In a Garrison show you play to audiences who recognize the best when they see it. I know because I've spent much more time training audiences than I ever have training actors. You sing new songs and act in new sketches, and you work alongside the men who wrote them. You have no idea what that's like because up to now you've never had the chance to find out. Everything in a pierrot show is rotten with age before the pierrots ever get their hands on it."

"It's no good, Mr. Garrison," Gladys said. "I can't come. We—we stay together, you see."

Garrison sat down. "Gladys, you are the first person in ten years to turn down one of my offers. That is something of a distinction. In return I'm going to say something to you that so far as I can re-

Part V

member I've never said before to any actress. If you ever change your mind, I'll give you a job. Now get out."

Gladys grabbed her hat and coat and fled. While she was at Miss Wilson's desk putting them on, the house telephone rang. Miss Wilson answered quickly. She said: "Yes, Mr. Garrison. Yes, I will." Then she turned to Gladys: "Mr. Garrison wants me to pay your expenses."

Benny, Blanche, Cookie and (surprisingly) Bobbie Brown were on the platform at Skunby-on-Sea when Gladys' train pulled in. Gladys sprang from a first-class carriage and was immediately caught by Benny. Cookie whistled. "First class! First class! Sorry we ain't got no red carpet."

"It's Mr. Garrison's money," Gladys babbled. "He paid for everything. I had me dinner on the train. Three puddings."

"Three puddings, and you twenty-eight!"

"What's twenty-eight got to do with it? They was all fluff, and none bigger than a one-bite gob."

8

BENNY, as Blanche had surmised, felt extremely proud of his wife, but not after he learned what had happened at her interview with Garrison. During the hours that followed Gladys' return to Buena Vista, it seemed as if between them the Buckells took an ax to the weak tree that was their marriage and cut it down for good. As usual, they had the greatest difficulty in making themselves clear to each other, and Gladys' efforts to placate her husband only succeeded in infuriating him further ("After all, London ain't a particularly *healthy* place to live, you know, Benny. And Skunby's so bracin'. . . .")

Benny shouted: "You should have said yes to *anything* Garrison suggested! How could you have been so idiotic as to imagine that he of all people would want to employ the entire Glad Rags company? What are we—a ladies' choir, or something?"

"But we've said all along that whatever happened we'd stay together. We've often talked of it."

"That was *us*, Gladys. You and me."

"And not my sixteen sisters. I see." There was an unaccustomed edge to her voice.

Benny spoke slowly and carefully, as if he were addressing a stupid child. "Can't you see what you've done? You've made us miss the first big chance we've ever had. If Garrison thinks as highly of you as he seems to—I've never heard of any producer offering an unknown actress a job that she can pick up any time she cares to ask for it— you could have talked him into a joint contract if you'd really wanted. Women manage these things. And it's not as if you didn't owe me something, after all these years. If we'd had a double act in the first place the way I wanted, instead of the Variety Three that you insisted on, we might have had a Garrison contract long ago. But you know what you are—always dragging your family in."

"Dragging my family in!" Gladys was shouting now. "If you think I'd tell Mr. Garrison one thing, when I meant something quite different, you're running in the wrong dog's lane."

"I apologize. I'd forgotten what a Sunday school girl you are. Deceiving anyone's a sin, isn't it?"

"I don't mind deceiving people if I got good reason. The point is —I got to *have* good reason, and you ain't it. What does it matter where you and I work? People are people other places besides London, ain't they? And another thing," she continued. "When we formed the Glad Rags, we did it partly so us girls could work together, remember? If you and I went to London, what would happen to the Glad Rags? What would happen to my sisters?"

They continued in this vein for some time. At last Benny changed his tune. When he spoke next, his voice had a whine in it. "Glad," he said, "it's proper for a man and wife to have calls on each other. You must see that. But the girls, they've got husbands of their own, all except Blanche. Why can't you leave them to look after themselves?"

"Because they can't," Gladys cried. "You've taught them to depend on me, just the way you do."

And with that she threw herself across her bed, sobbing.

It was true, of course. The Miller sisters managed well enough all together in the Glad Rags, but aside from Gladys, none of them would have lasted long in any other show—not even Flo, now that her chief interest was her family. As for the girls' husbands, Jamie

Leake was not strong enough to do a full day's work; Billy Dyer, shouting *"Quiet"* in his film studio, was, as Benny had said, unlikely ever to make much of a living; and Tom Holt was the right man in the right job only so long as a second-rate man was what was needed. Blanche had no husband so far, and she was capable enough when she wasn't off attending prayer meetings or sitting up half the night drying the tears of penniless drama students. (Where would that end, Benny thought crossly. For that matter, where was it now? Religious women made their own rules, just like the others.)

But in considering three of the Miller girls' husbands, Benny could not avoid casting a glance in the direction of the fourth. He himself was no better than the rest. For years he had been hoping to climb into a London show on his wife's talent, since it had been proved long ago that he had insufficient of his own.

Disgusted with everybody and everything, Benny slammed out of the house. It was evening already—the whole afternoon had been lost in quarreling. The wind had risen, and Benny had to fight his way along the lane that led past the deserted shacks. Finding no one that he knew in the half-empty bars along the esplanade, Benny returned to Buena Vista. By now it was dark. Blanche was in the kitchen, ironing. He refused the plate of congealed fish and chips she offered him for his supper.

Upstairs, Benny found Gladys lying exactly as he had left her. He undressed slowly, hoping that she would say something. He felt tired and lonely and old and a failure. The smallest apology on her part would have sufficed. But she didn't speak, and he wasn't going to be the first to. By the time he got into bed, she still hadn't said anything. So he didn't either. Or touch her.

9

DESPITE what is generally believed about unhappy years, the next four years passed quickly for Gladys. She had not been brought up to look on personal happiness as a right, and consequently when things went wrong, it did not occur to her to indulge in self-pity. She schooled herself to cheerfulness, at least so far as appearances were concerned, and did it so successfully that nobody in the Glad Rags thought of feeling sorry for her.

Benny's consoling friendships were of a kind that frequently ended with the last girl but one pouring her troubles into Gladys' sympathetic ears. The stories varied so little that it was all Gladys could do not to prompt the girl if for any reason she fluffed her lines.

Her attitude annoyed her sisters. "If Glad had any pride," Lily said to her husband, "she'd throw Benny out. We don't need him."

"Gladys does, though," Jamie replied.

This was true. Where work was concerned, Benny was as generous with his help and as painstaking as ever. On the rare occasions when they differed on a point and Gladys stood her ground, he would yield, but he still made all the decisions. No tiny change of a movement, no minute alteration to a costume was effected unless Benny approved. This situation remained the same even when their domestic difficulties were at their worst. One girl threatened to take Benny to court, a course of action which would have ruined the Glad Rags in the sedate, law-abiding North. While the whole company was on tenterhooks, Gladys spent a morning with Benny discussing earrings. Did these long pendants she had found in Woolworth's look funnier from the front than the discs she had been wearing hitherto?

"Glad's got no sense of decency at all," was Flo's comment.

"The tragedy is," Blanche added, "she's in *love* with her husband."

These years had their compensations. A new generation was growing up. In 1931, Edith's twins, Dolly and Ruth, were born, and now Holly and Fred had more grandchildren than daughters. The eldest of these, Flo's boy Launcelot, was now five, and already busy cadging scrumps from the fish-and-chip men—the pieces of batter that float off while the fish is being cooked, and which are given away free to children. Launcelot's sister Marge was three, and Cyril, the most recent arrival in the Dyer family, one. (Flo chose the fancy names, Billy the alternate.) With the exception of four-year-old Jamie Leake, who had looked like one of his own ancestors when he was born and never even seemed much younger, the next generation was turning out just as vigorous and undisciplined a brood as their mothers and aunts had been.

Part V

The sisters' homes and family lives were Gladys' to share, and she could rely on Cookie's devotion. Cookie by this time was almost as much a member of the Miller clan as if he belonged to it: Gladys' efforts to discourage him met with no success. ("All right, so I'm wasting my time, and you ain't going to divorce Benny Buckell, and even if you were, you wouldn't marry me. I heard you. Now let me tell *you* something. I'm forty-four, and most of that time I've been looking for a wife. We start everything early where I come from. But from now on I'm not looking any more. I'm looking at you instead. There's no law against that, not against looking, there isn't.")

All this was comforting, but the show was more comforting still. Once inside the theater (or whatever passed for a theater when the Glad Rags were on tour) Gladys' gaiety, which a great deal of the time in real life was an act, ceased to be pretense. The thrill as well as the satisfaction were there, whether she sang "The Lord's Prayer" very slowly under a purple spot or, smothered in flashy "jewels" and a great cartwheel hat with feathers on it, persuaded the audience to join her in:

> The ballroom was filled with fashion's throng,
> It shone with a thousand lights,
> And there was a woman who passed along,
> The fairest of all the sights.
> A girl to her lover then softly sighed
> "There's riches at her command,"
> "But she married for wealth, not for love," he cried,
> "Though she lives in a mansion grand:
>
> She's only a bird in a gilded cage,
> A beautiful sight to see,
> You may think she's happy and free from care,
> She's not, though she seems to be,
> 'Tis sad when you think of her wasted life,
> For youth cannot mate with age,
> And her beauty was sold for an old man's gold,
> She's a bird in a gilded cage."

Skunby-on-Sea was a better dressed town these days than it had been in Joe Lansbury's time. The young girls brought a whole wardrobe of cotton dresses with them to wear under their overcoats as they walked on the esplanade, and the older women had silk stockings showing through the slits in their white holiday sandals. (The men's clothes had not changed: open-necked shirts, gray flannel trousers, green or blue jackets and peaked caps to match.) Making their way past the trashcans labeled TEA LEAVES ONLY and the sign outside the pier office which said CLOAKROOM. LOST CHILDREN, the crowds would pour into the Glad Rags' theater, to applaud Gladys until their hands were sore, and scream with delight when Benny, jumping down from the stage, embraced one of the more ample ladies spread over a seat on the center aisle. Benny would then return to the stage, and say: "Well! That *was* nice."

COOKIE: It looked it, I must say.
BENNY: Why don't *you* go down and have a nibble?
COOKIE: Shall I? Which one?
BENNY: (*pointing*): *That* one.
COOKIE: She's got her husband with her.
BENNY: Never mind her husband.
COOKIE: I do mind. I mustn't get in a fight. I'm meeting my girl after the show.
BENNY: You are?
COOKIE: Yes. She'll be waiting for me outside the school.
BENNY: Teacher?
COOKIE: Dear me, no! That wasn't necessary. . . .

After the show—and the handshaking and autograph signing—Cookie would wait for Gladys at the stage door and see her home. He usually had to wait a long time. Gladys was always slow changing back into her street clothes.

10

ON NOVEMBER 5, 1605, a convert to Roman Catholicism named Guy Fawkes arranged to blow up the Protestant King James I and the members of the Lords and Commons while the official opening of Parliament was going on. The plot failed, but the English, who become attached to their political criminals, have celebrated Guy Fawkes Day ever since. Children dress up in fancy costume, bonfires blaze in back yards, chestnuts are roasted and snapdragons (lacy, sticky ginger cookies made in the form of hollow tubes) eaten, while the father of the family sets off firecrackers and fireworks.

In 1932, Guy Fawkes Day fell on a Sunday, so most bonfire parties were held the night before. That week end, the Glad Rags were appearing in a small theater in the downtown industrial district of Sheffield, a steel city in Yorkshire. They gave two performances each on the Friday and Saturday evenings, at six P.M. and at nine.

The Glad Rags had never played Sheffield before, and one reason why they were pleased with the booking was that they were able to stay at Arcadia, a theatrical rooming house reputed to be the most comfortable north of the Trent.

Arcadia wasn't much to look at—a dingy, blackened brick house fronting on a street that had trams running down it—but the landlady, Mrs. Berry, was an old pro, and she knew exactly how to take care of the somewhat specialized needs of her guests. She was a jolly woman with a red face and a ringing laugh, and in a matter of minutes she was on the best of terms with the entire company. The Glad Rags responded with a lavish allotment of free seats, and Mrs. Berry attended all four shows, bringing with her a bevy of rowdy, appreciative companions.

The Glad Rags, since they were new in the town, put on a program of "safe" numbers—songs and sketches that had been proved successful elsewhere. These included a stutterer. A stuttering man never fails to draw laughter from a concert-party audience, and a stuttering cockney (Cookie played the part) had the Sheffield crowds rolling in their seats—a local accent, if it is local somewhere else, is as safe a bet as the stutterer himself. The Glad Rags program also included a pair of quite good can-can dancers; Lily, in a crimson velvet gown, played her concertina; and Tom Holt and Gladys, in straw boaters, sang "A Bicycle Built for Two."

The nine o'clock show on Saturday night was attended by a group of delegates to a hairdressers' convention who gave Gladys a rousing ovation every time she appeared. Their enthusiasm puzzled the Glad Rags until, after the performance was over, they met the man responsible for bringing the hairdressers to the theater. He was Madame Lola's husband, Frank Beggs.

Gladys was delighted to see him, as she always was to see anyone even remotely connected with Tor. Frankie hadn't changed much. He was fatter, and his curly hair was quite gray, but he still looked prosperous and jaunty, and he smelled strongly of heather perfume. "I don't understand this," Gladys said. "I thought you was in shampoo."

"Ah," Frank replied, "I been promoted since then. Men's toiletries is my line now."

The hairdressers (there were ten of them) had no particular plans for the remainder of the evening, so the whole party, with the exception of Benny Buckell, adjourned to Arcadia, where Mrs. Berry had a Guy Fawkes bonfire party. Cookie and Tom helped to let off fireworks, Mrs. Berry dispensed hot pies, and in between explosions and eating, everyone sang Christmas carols.

"How's Madame?" Gladys asked.

"Lovely as ever," Frank replied. "She misses the school, though."

"Don't she have it no more? I hadn't heard."

Frank shook his head. "The girls come over here. Sheffield's got a charm school."

Gladys burst out laughing.

"You'd laugh twice as big if you could see the girls," Frank continued. "The only ones as could learn anything don't sign up. Like Gladys Miller, for instance. You should've heard what the boys said about you tonight. Blushed for you, I did."

"You might have blushed for yourself," Gladys said. "What's kept you away from the show all this time? This is our tenth winter on the road."

"It ain't for want of trying. You don't know the number of times I've come into a town on a toilet call, only to find the Glad Rags has just been, or else is to come next week. And Skunby's out of the question for us. Sea air brings Loly out in a rash."

"Well, we'll just have to make up for lost time now," Gladys said cheerfully. "We're going to be here over the week end. Our next booking's only Glossop, and there's no sense in moving from Arcadia any sooner than we need. How about you?"

Frank pulled a long face. "I'll be here too, but we've got a convention lunch tomorrow, *and* a do in the afternoon. Sunday night's free, though. What about a bit of supper?" He paused, and then added politely, "Mr. Buckell too, of course, if he'd care to come."

"Whee!" was Gladys' answer. "I don't know *how* long it is since anybody took me out! I don't know about Benny though, Frank. He always has so much to do at the week ends—business, and that. But I'll ask him, and if he can't get, you'll just have to manage the best you can with me."

The hairdressers and the Glad Rags parted company shortly after midnight. Benny was already in bed when Gladys came up to their room. She told him about Frank's invitation. Benny said: "I'm flattered to be asked, but I shan't come."

"Why not? We'd love to have you."

"I wouldn't want to spoil Frankie's romantic evening."

"I'll say. Frank Beggs, of all people!"

Benny yawned. "Well, don't let him talk you into giving a benefit performance for the Chesterfield School of Voice. You know what you are."

"Madame don't have a school no more."

Benny ignored this. "Any outfit within a fifty-mile radius of Tor gets a free show out of you for the asking, I notice, irrespective of how expensive or inconvenient it is for the rest of us."

"That's a lie!" Gladys shouted. "The only time I ever agreed to a free show without consulting you first was at the New Cut Welfare, and then—"

"The New Cut Welfare! My God, shall I ever forget the New Cut Welfare!"

It was months since the Buckells had had a quarrel, and now they thoroughly let themselves go. They were as rude and cruel to each other as they knew how to be, and, after their anger was spent, as tender and as loving. Always before, this physically satisfactory ending to a row had seemed enough, but tonight it occurred to Gladys that Holly's advice—"Whatever Benny does, just see to it that you have a laugh and a cuddle for him when he wants it"—might not contain the whole of the answer. "Benny, love," she said, "couldn't we go off somewhere and spend the day, you and me? Blanche'll have dinner with Frank for me. We're always so busy— we get so little time to be alone."

"Darling, I can't," Benny answered. "I've an appointment."

"With a beautiful woman?"

"Of course."

11

ALL the same, Gladys enjoyed her dinner with Frank very much. As she had said, it was a long time since anyone had taken her out, and Frank did everything in style. He arrived at Arcadia five minutes ahead of the time they had arranged to meet, carrying an orchid corsage in a little box, and he had already reserved a restaurant table—not at one of the large uptown hotels, as Benny would have done, but in a small basement place that served beer and excellent roast beef. They took a long time over their meal. During its course, Gladys learned that in spite of giving up her school, Madame Lola was as active as ever, and still enjoying frequent headaches and dizzy spells. She had replaced teaching with vegetarianism, sun-lamp treatment, and "Ethics by Mail." These demanded such close and strenuous attention, Frank indicated (in tones in which admiration and regret were nicely mixed), that Madame found it necessary to spend the greater part of each day on her chaise longue.

Frank, however, knew how to listen as well as talk. Gladys found him an appreciative audience. Unlike Benny, he did not expect her to behave like a lady—when she whistled shrilly through her fingers to attract their waiter's attention, he laughed.

"Do you get to Chesterfield at all on this tour?" he asked.

"It's our last town before Christmas, I think. Why?"

"I wonder," Frank hesitated. "D'you think you could possibly find time to give a little show for Lola while you're there? She admires you so much, and she can't ever get to theaters. Crowds tire her."

They didn't tire her when it was her musical afternoons, Gladys thought. Aloud, she said, "Oh Frank, I don't know! *I* wouldn't mind, but Benny does. We went to the New Cut Welfare a couple of months ago (they paid my way the first six months I was at Madame's, you know), and Benny didn't like us going at all. He don't feel the way you and I do, you see, about obliging old friends."

Frank was sympathetic. "Well, Loly's certainly an old friend of yours. She always says you were the pick of all her pupils."

"Me?"

"Ever since you made a name for yourself, she's had a big framed picture of you in her bedroom."

"Frank! You must be joking!"

"See for yourself when you go there."

"Blow me down, mother. Blow me down."

"So if you *could* stretch a point in her case—"

"I will. Benny'll slay me, but I will."

The dessert was rhubarb and cream.

"Like a second go? It's allowed," Frank said.

"I don't mind if I do," Gladys replied.

Watching his gray, carefully greased curls as he sat concentrating on his pudding, Gladys felt sorry for Frank Beggs, tied for life to silly sick Madame.

Frank looked up and caught her eye. "You look beautiful tonight," he said.

"The beer's gone to your head," Gladys answered amiably. "Beautiful I never shall be."

Cautiously, Frank reached a chubby paw across the table that separated them. Gladys took it and held it and smiled at him. Frank said: "What would you like to do now? We can go the round of the bars, or we can go to my room."

"Let's go to your room," Gladys said at once. "I know what bars are like on Sundays. Thronged."

Frank rose. "I'll have to telephone first—you don't mind? Where I stay, women ain't normally allowed."

"Oh well, in that case, don't bother. We'll do the bars."

But Frank was already across the small room at the telephone booth, fumbling in his pocket for a coin.

Before they left, Frank insisted on buying a bottle of Empire Ruby port. ("Floats nice on top of anything, Empire Ruby does," he told her.)

Outside, it was damp. They had some distance to walk. Frank took Gladys' arm, and they made their way cozily together past small yards where Sabbath-breakers were happily celebrating Guy Fawkes Day on the right date. There were bonfires everywhere, and groups of excited children. After a while, they reached a quiet street of small row houses, each of which had a flight of stone steps leading from the sidewalk to its front door. Frank's house was in the middle of the block, and his front door was unlocked. Just inside, in a dimly lighted hall, a woman lolled in a rocking chair, and Gladys was startled to see that in the place on her bosom where she might have worn a brooch, she was wearing a live canary. The woman dozed, while the little bird pecked briskly, stepping about among the frills and folds of her blouse. The woman ignored Gladys, but she nodded to Frank, and as he passed she took some grains of seed out of her pocket and tossed them at her bosom. The canary reeled, and then resumed its pecking.

Frank's room was upstairs, at the back. It was a very small, extremely clean room, hung with flounced cretonne curtains. It contained a double bed, a chair and a marble-topped washstand with a china jug and basin and two small tumblers on it. A circular mirror and a calendar depicting a basketful of kittens hung on the loudly flowered walls.

Frank set the bottle of Empire Ruby carefully on the mantelpiece and took off his raincoat. Then he walked over to the washstand and picked up the tumblers. As he did so, Gladys (it was indeed time) realized where she was.

For a very brief moment it was all she could do not to laugh. One of those deep-seated guffaws that had been such an embarrassment to all of them at the Chesterfield School of Voice came welling up inside her at the picture the two of them presented beside the bottle of Empire Ruby in this bright, discreet room—Madame Lola's aging heather-smelling husband, and Mrs. Benny Buckell, who would be thirty-three next May.

When you think of the people you knew when you were a child, Gladys thought, you think of them in the same way that you have always thought of them. You forget that as a grown person, you seem, because you are, quite different to them. While she had dined with old Madame Lola's old husband, Frank Beggs had dined with an actress (a star actress) whose husband was off on his own somewhere, and who had herself elected to accompany him to this room.

"Frank," Gladys said, "this isn't where you're staying, is it?"

Frank had his back to her. "I'm at the Y," he mumbled. "It's like I told you. Women can't go there." He should have said no more, but he made the mistake of adding, "I'm lonely."

The effect of these two small words was devastating. All Gladys' gentleness and sweetness, or what he had taken for those qualities, fell from her like a cloak.

"*Lonely!*" He was appalled by the loudness and clarity of her voice. "*You're* lonely! What d'you suppose *I* am? What d'you suppose most women are? Listen, Frank—" She came over and with the irritable gesture of one disciplining a puppy, she grasped the lapels of his jacket. "Don't you know what loneliness is? It's teeth—*baby's* teeth. Nobody likes cutting them, but we all have to if we're ever going to grow up." Dropping her hands, she continued more quietly, "Just take a look at the people who let themselves stay lonely—that ought to stop you, if nothing else does. Look at the rotten performances they give! I see them over and over in the theater, and Blanche meets them in the churches she goes to. Both places is full of lonely people packed in like fish, each one in a separate tin. They all think God owes them something, instead of it being the other way around."

Frank was furious. "You're a fine one to preach!" he cried, his evening splintered about him. "What d'you know about loneliness? When d'you ever get as much as five minutes alone?"

"Oh, Frank. Being *with* people's got nothing to do with it."

"Well, all I can say is—" Frank Beggs was a great man for clichés —"life's a hard road."

"I know it is, but after all, why shouldn't it be? Who said life had to be anything *but* hard?" She grinned at his red, discomfited face. "You're right, though; I've no call to preach."

Firmly, she picked up Frank's raincoat, and held it for him while he put it on. Frank gathered up the bottle of Empire Ruby, holding it the way a child holds a favorite doll, as if protecting himself with its closeness. Together, they made their way downstairs. The woman in the rocking chair was still there. She did not stir as they passed her. The canary had disappeared.

Out on the sidewalk, Gladys took Frank's arm. "Let's sing," she said.

"Singing in the street ain't respectable," Frank replied.

"Hymns is all right. In fact, I should think in *this* street a few hymns—"

"Gladys. *Please* . . ."

Frank only spoke twice on the walk back to Arcadia. Once he

said: "You won't feel like doing that little concert for Lola now, will you?"

"Of course I will. I'll go and see Madame the minute we get to Chesterfield."

The second time was as they were about to turn a corner within a few yards of Mrs. Berry's. "I'll leave you here. It mightn't do for the others to see you out with me so late."

"Nobody'll be sitting up for me," Gladys replied.

But with one exception, all of them were. The Glad Rags crowded Arcadia's doorway, and with them was a policeman, and Mrs. Berry in tears.

12

FRANK slipped away—whatever might lie ahead in no way concerned him. Gladys already knew. In Tor, when the policeman called at a house as late at night as this, it was for one purpose—to tell the family that there had been a fatal accident. And the only member of the Glad Rags concert party missing from the group in the doorway was Benny Buckell.

So when the policeman, a young fellow acutely embarrassed by his assignment, told Gladys that her husband was dead, she nodded, and the first thing she thought to say was that she was sorry he had had to be the bearer of the news.

Benny Buckell had been killed in an automobile accident some miles outside the city, when the car in which he was traveling took a corner too fast. The driver of the car, a Mrs. Janey Kershaw, had also been killed. (Mrs. Kershaw, the policeman said, owned a charm school.) The deaths had, it was thought, occurred instantaneously, for the car was found off the road against a wall, and both bodies were badly burned.

So the charm school had been Janey's—Mrs. Janey Kershaw, who had once been Mrs. Benny Buckell. Gladys had almost forgotten about Janey, the manicurist from Sheffield who was only too likely by this time, of course, to have aspired to charm, and a fast car, and a renewal of interest in her former husband.

Later, when the policeman had left, Gladys telephoned Martin

Hay. ("He'll be asleep," Blanche demurred. "I know, but he'd a lot rather be woke than not told," Gladys said.)

Meanwhile, Mrs. Berry made the Glad Rags a big pot of tea and built up the kitchen fire. Then she went to bed, leaving the company to sit up with Gladys. None offered her sympathy, but as they sat silently around Arcadia's kitchen, stirring their mugs of hot tea, they comforted her much, for it occurred to Gladys, bewildered and wretched as she was, that here, right at this table, lay another chance. These people needed her just as Benny had done, and perhaps if one were lucky one need not fail twice.

With Martin Hay's help, Gladys arranged for a joint burial in Tor (Janey Kershaw had no family). The funeral service was conducted by the rector and attended by two ladies employed at the charm school, and by Fred and Holly Miller. Gladys and the others stayed out with the Glad Rags' tour.

13

GLADYS found the remaining six weeks of the company's autumn engagement an alarming experience. She was shocked by Benny's death, and frightened of the responsibilities she had to shoulder. The others tried to help her, but she would not let them. She insisted on seeing to everything herself—the billing, the box-office returns, the traveling arrangements, the program, the rehearsals—she did it all. At first she tried to engage another artiste to take Benny's place, but no one suitable could be found so near the opening of the Christmas pantomime season. The company tried to be patient, but Gladys was extremely difficult to work with, and all of them looked forward to December 20, when their season would close. To fill the gap in the cast that Benny had left, Gladys insisted, against the advice of Cookie and Tom, on inserting an item that was always popular at Skunby-on-Sea. The men in the audience were invited to come up on the stage, roll up their trouser-legs and compete for a prize which the Glad Rags offered to the owner of the most knobbly pair of knees. But the bare male knee, laughable though it may appear beside the seaside in August, looks naked and out of place inland in the wintertime, and the number was not a success. Even the staple joke routines seemed to fall flat:

COOKIE: I just had a seven-course dinner.

TOM: Seven-course dinner! What did you have?

COOKIE: Six chips and a fish.

TOM: Well, now I should think you're ready for an Adam and Eve cigarette.

COOKIE: Adam and Eve cigarette! What are they?

TOM: Oh, you know *them*. When you've Adam, you Eve. . . .

Gladys kept her promise to Frank Beggs, and when the Glad Rags reached Chesterfield for their final engagement of the tour, she arranged a short private show for Madame Lola. Frank was out of town, but he had warned his wife and she was expecting them. Looking thin and mad in a pink teagown to which baby-blue ribbons were attached, she wept to see Gladys again, and went into ecstasies over the Glad Rags' performance. Her joy depressed the company more than anything that had happened since Benny died.

For the first time in their history, the Glad Rags dispensed with their customary end-of-tour party on the stage (beer and sausages, and a concert in which the doormen and stagehands were invited to join). When the last curtain fell, Tom Holt left at once for South Wales, where he had several Christmas engagements to fulfill, and Cookie caught the night train to Grimsby, where he was to play in pantomime. The others stayed over for a day to pack the tabs, props and costumes, and ship them to Buena Vista. That done, the Miller contingent caught the bus home to Tor. All of them were very tired.

14

IT WAS several Christmases since the Millers had all been at home together. There wasn't room for everyone at The Nag's Head Inn, and the Dyers stayed with Lily and Jamie at Leake Revel. There were now four children in the Dyer family—the youngest, Bert (his father had chosen that name), was four months old. The Dowager Lady Leake was delighted with this avalanche of Christmas visitors —she did not mind the noise, and their muddle she liked. Only one of her own daughters was home. Margaret Smalley-Rivers was in India with her family, but Catherine had come. Catherine Leake, a plump, cheerful woman of thirty-five, had achieved her ambition and become a doctor. She practiced in London, in a poor neighborhood near Euston Station.

The Millers, as they always did when they returned to Tor, entered at once into all the village activities they could. Gladys sang her old part in Martin Hay's production of *The Messiah*, and over the holiday, all five daughters helped their father in The Nag's Head bar. Fred was very glad to have them.

These days, when anyone inquired for the innkeeper's health, Fred always replied, "Middlin', thanks," which from a Derbyshire man means he is feeling fine, but middlin' was an exaggeration in Fred's case. Well below the middle would have been nearer the mark. After Rose Dutton married, he hadn't seemed able to find satisfactory barmaids any more. Rose, like his own girls, had known how to gossip in a leisurely fashion and work fast at the same time. Holly of course could be relied on—she was full of energy; but Holly couldn't do everything, though she certainly liked to try.

Fred did not worry too much about his failing health, but he did worry about his job. The Manley Brewery wanted to buy The Nag's Head, and they had made him a good offer. (The Manley Brewery brewed the bulk of the beer that The Nag's Head sold, and they were buying up inns all over the country.) If Fred sold out, he could stay on as an employee, doing just as much work as he wanted to, and without, of course, an innkeeper's responsibilities. Fred didn't know what to do. He had the feeling that he ought to sell, but he dreaded doing so. When he talked the matter over with Holly, she had said at once that selling the inn—selling *anything*— was better than for Fred to make himself ill. But he had scared her, he knew, for right afterward she'd added (rather sharply) that if Fred had only put on one side the money he'd been paying the Pearl Assurance all these years, they'd have had enough saved to retire to a bungalow somewhere—Skunby-on-Sea, perhaps! Fred had smiled at that. Holly never had grown used to his loyalty to the Pearl Assurance. The collector still came for his money on the first Saturday afternoon of each month—there'd been a whole series of collectors since Mr. Murphy's time. So Fred didn't say any more about selling the inn, but he didn't give the Manley people a definite refusal, either. He told them he'd think some more about it, and then let them know.

For Gladys, there could have been no better place than Tor in which to spend this Christmas and the weeks that followed. She needed time to regain her balance after the shock of Benny's death. She had hoped (doggedly) that her marriage would right itself somehow, but it had not, and now the opportunity was gone. It was a grueling and painful experience for her to have to admit, after it was too late, that she had devoted the least time and the fewest thoughts to the relationship she cared the most about.

On the practical side, Gladys was, like Fred, not sure what she ought to do next. It seemed out of the question not to continue the Glad Rags, and yet, if the last six weeks were any indication, without Benny to guide it, the company seemed sure to fail.

The people of Tor left Gladys severely alone. No one came forward with helpful advice or sympathy or asked her about her plans. If the Miller sisters wondered about the future, they did not say so, and Holly and Fred were far too happy with their children and grandchildren around them to ask how long they might stay.

Except for a newly painted barn here and there, a new gate or a rebuilt field wall, Tor looked to Gladys just the way it always had. The children playing on the gibbet steps were different children, of course, and now it was Mr. Crew instead of Daniel Park who recited the adventures of the Thumperlumps and the Wobbligobs, and Launcelot and his sister Marge who listened, instead of Edith and Flo. Up at the Poole house, Mrs. John instead of Lucy cooked the weekly meal and laced the tea with whisky. At the school, instead of Miss Piper and her niece Miss Ethel, it was two sisters from Wales, one of whom was very deaf, who attempted (with no more success than the Pipers had had) to bring the children and a little learning together. Among those who had not altered (except that his limp was more pronounced) was the rector. "You get 'Rock of Ages' sung as well these days as I used to sing it, Mr. Hay?" Gladys asked him.

"Much better," the rector replied. "Dessie Bagworth attends rehearsals."

But the most comforting of the changeless elements in Tor was the wetness of the weather. This Christmas, it was very mild. The air felt warm, and weighed down with water. Day after day, little black clouds scudded across a sky which overhung the village like a roof of thick gray wool. With Tor so securely blanketed, it seemed almost as if time itself was excluded from the valley.

Time broke through, though, and sharply, toward the end of January. Cookie, on finishing his pantomime engagement, came at once to Tor, and he did not hesitate to ask what the Glad Rags' plans were.

He was not surprised to learn that so far they had none. Blanche told him that two offers of work had come in, but no reply had been made to either letter. There was also a letter from Mrs. Pegler, asking if Gladys would care to buy Buena Vista. A vaudeville artistes' charity in London wanted the house for an old people's home. "We've been trying to sell for I don't know how long," Mrs. Pegler wrote, "but nobody would have the place on account of that clown in the fun fair. The vaudeville folk won't mind him any more than you do. All that laughter will just make the place seem more homey."

Cookie made no comment on this correspondence, but he did take some action. Gathering the Glad Rags together in the inn kitchen, he produced, out of the ancient suitcase with which he always traveled, a large sheet of bright red writing paper and an envelope to match. Handing these to Gladys, he said: "Them's for writing Mr. Garrison on."

"Mr. Garrison! What's come over you, Cookie?"

"While I bin away," Cookie replied, "I made three discoveries. One: we can't any of us live on love and fresh water, not even me. We've got to work. Two: Gladys can't manage the Glad Rags, not without Benny, and we can't manage the Glad Rags without Glad. So—we got to find something else to do. Three: Garrison, Glad's friend with the nice job in London any time she likes to ask for it, is casting a new show. So all Glad has to do is get busy, *now*, before it's too late."

"Cookie," Gladys said, "there's one thing you've forgotten. When Mr. Garrison said he'd give me a job, he said me, not the Glad Rags."

"I know, but when you've been in this business as long as I have, you'll know that there's only one thing an actor can be sure of, and that is that no producer ever says the same thing two days together, let alone two weeks, and it's been more than four *years* since Mr. Garrison talked to you."

"So what d'you suggest?"

"That you go and see him and remind him of his promise, only when you do, don't remind him of it quite exact, see?"

"No, I don't."

Cookie tried another bait. He yawned. "I expect you're right. Ten to one Garrison's forgotten all about you by now. After all, it *was* four years ago."

The fish rose. "He'll have done no such thing! He ain't that kind of man."

"All right, then. What harm is there in you asking for jobs for us? If he won't give us any, we're no worse off than we are now, and if he will, we're up to our necks in gravy."

Gladys laughed. Cookie's cockney accent, cutting in over the slow Derbyshire voices and through the isolation in which all of them were wrapped, excited her. It was indeed time she went to work again. Cookie had brought the smell of the theater into the inn with him.

That night, the following letter went out from Tor on the big sheet of red paper:

THE NAG'S HEAD INN
TOR, DERBYSHIRE
January 29, 1933

DEAR MR. GARRISON,

With reference to our conversation of September, 1928, I should like to discuss this matter further and will call at your office Wednesday next at eleven A.M.

The reason for this paper is that I am coming to London specially to see you and I do not want to be overlooked.

Yours respectfully,

GLADYS MILLER
(the late Mrs. Benny Buckell)

It was decided that Lily, Cookie and Tom Holt should accompany Gladys to London, thus giving George Garrison an opportunity to see a representative Glad Rags offering if he wished to do so. At the last moment, Blanche said she would go too, not to meet Garrison, but to hear the Reverend Fox, who was holding a series of religious meetings that week in a Mayfair hotel.

Lily said to Gladys: "Where will we stay? *Not* that place where Jamie's Ma takes us—tiny portions at meals, and turkeys in the radiators. Ours gobbled all night."

Cookie assured her that he knew of a theatrical hotel where they would be as comfortable as they had been at Arcadia. Blanche wrote down the address for Holly, and put it where the Millers always put their valuables, on the shelf at the back of the bar.

When they were ready to leave, Fred said to Gladys: "If that fellow Garrison's got nothing for thee, tha'll come right on home? The Nag's Head don't pay its barmaids much, but the boss—he's a wonder to work for."

15

THE NAG'S HEAD was not usually busy on Tuesdays, but the Tuesday Gladys and the others left for London, Fred and Holly were rushed off their feet all evening. The reason was that the Tor bell ringers had had a meet in the late afternoon with teams from two neighboring villages—Bunny and Tibshelf—and after the contest, the whole group came to The Nag's Head for hot pies and beer. Fred built a great fire to welcome them, and all stayed until closing time, which was good for business, but a strain on the innkeeper. When he had seen the last customer off the premises and tidied up, Fred felt worn out. Holly said: "Don't stay long over thy prayers, love. We're both tired."

Fred sighed. "I could ha' done with six pairs of hands tonight."

When she had gone upstairs, he sat down in his usual place under the bull's head. He hadn't even the energy to draw his usual tankard of ale. He was used to his back and legs aching after a day's work, but tonight he had a pain in his chest as well. Slowly, it came to Fred that if he had been looking for a sign, this was it. He must give up the inn. He hadn't the right to make himself a burden to his family, and he'd be ill if he went through another night like tonight. His decision depressed him. He had always disliked change, and at the moment it seemed as if the effort of selling would be more of a tax on his strength than trying to carry on. But he must sell and since he must, he'd be given the strength, he was sure of that. ("God . . . will not suffer you to be tempted above that you are able; but will with the temptation also make a way of escape, that ye may be able to bear it.")

Fred looked around him. The dying firelight shone on the neat rows of glasses and polished tankards, on the sides of the dark counter, and on the dowdy old bull's head. Close to where he sat, there were marks on the wall that recorded the heights of his daughters—short horizontal pencil lines marched sturdily upward. He'd tell Holly tonight about selling the inn, and in the morning he'd use that telephone, and call the Manley Brewery.

Fred must have dozed off. When he came to, the fire was dead. His feet and hands felt cold. Get along, he told himself. Say thy prayers and off to bed before the night freezes thee. But for the life of him he couldn't remember any prayers. All he could think of was the twenty-third psalm, and this for some reason he had a great desire to sing. With the kind of voice he had, singing by himself in the empty bar in the middle of the night didn't half sound daft! (Or it would have, except that everyone else was singing.)

16

GLADYS, Lily and Blanche received the news of Fred's death by telephone at six o'clock that morning. "Come as soon as you can," Edith said when she told them, "but *not* before you've seen Mr. Garrison."

"What d'you think we ought to do, Glad?" Lily asked after Edith rang off.

"I think we ought to do as Edie says," Gladys answered. "But you could go right now, Blanche. And tell Mum we'll be there just as soon as we can get."

It was therefore a very subdued little group that arrived at the Garrison office shortly before ten o'clock. Gladys was calm enough on the surface (a long time ago, Joe Lansbury had taught her to shut out of her mind everything that did not concern her work), but underneath she felt as nervous and keyed up as if a Glad Rags' show lay ahead of her, and in a sense, of course, it did.

Gladys' concentration, admirable though it was (she was determined not to think about Fred's death until after the interview was over), was not strong enough to stand any more shocks for a while, and three more awaited her at George Garrison's office. Garrison's secretary, Miss Wilson, whose kindness and friendliness Gladys remembered and was relying on, was nowhere to be seen. In her place sat a cool, impeccably dressed blonde, sleek as a kitten. On the blonde's desk was an open appointment book covered with writing, and beside it, in a wire basket with some other papers, Gladys' red envelope, not yet unsealed.

"Good morning," the kitten said. "What name?"

"Gladys Miller. I—"

"Have you an appointment?"

"Yes. No. That is—"

"Because I'm afraid Mr. Brodov can't see anyone without an appointment."

"Oh!" Gladys was relieved. "I haven't come to see Mr. Brodov. I've come to see Mr. Garrison."

"Mr. Garrison left twenty minutes ago for Paris, but if he asked you to call, that's quite all right. Mr. Brodov will see you."

The girl began looking through the names in the appointment book. Without any warning, Gladys burst into tears.

Crying as a decorative, or wheedling, art is unknown in Tor. In that village, when women cry, they do so solely to relieve their feelings, and they keep the noise up just as long as they need to. Gladys therefore made no effort to control the racket she was making, and Cookie, Tom and Lily made no effort either. They felt too much like bawling themselves. The blonde was furious. Just my luck, she thought, to have a bunch of hysterics drop in when Miss Wilson's at the dentist and Brodov in one of his moods!

Alexis Brodov, comfortably seated in Garrison's room a few yards away, was waiting for the one-cup percolator to prepare coffee. He was disturbed but in no way distressed by the sounds he heard through the thin wall. His horoscope that morning had told him that he would be given an early opportunity to do a distracted stranger a kindness, and it always pleased him when opportunity was punctual. He therefore opened the door, observed the scene without, and said to Gladys: "*Entrez, Madame.* I have a cup of coffee for you, just freshly made."

Gladys stopped crying. The voice—a soothing, foreign voice (Alexis Brodov had been born near the Caspian Sea)—emanated from a short, solid-looking man who was smiling sympathetically at her through thick spectacles. Without a word, she followed him into Garrison's room. Lily, Cookie and Tom followed her.

Alexis poured the coffee and handed the cup to Gladys. "Now," he said, "what is troubling you?"

Gladys told him. Alexis consulted his watch. "I have a meeting in ten minutes," he said, "but if you and your friends would like to sing to me till then, I will listen, and I will tell Mr. Garrison about you when he returns."

Gladys thanked him, and Cookie sat down at Garrison's piano (What a place London is, Lily thought. Even the offices have pianos in them!). With Lily's accordion accompaniment, and in their best Skunby style, the Glad Rags presented:

I have lived long enough to be rarely mistaken,
And had my full share of life's changeable scenes;
But my woes have been so laced by good greens and bacon
And my joys have been doubled by bacon and greens.

What a thrill of remembrance e'en now they awaken,
Of childhood's gay morning and youth's sunny scenes,
When one day we had greens and a plateful of bacon,
And the next we had bacon and a plateful of greens.

Alexis had his hands over his ears. "Look, my children," he began. But the Glad Rags never heard what it was they were to look at. A second voice, steely, commanding, and slightly nasal, overlaid his.

"Go back to the beginning, Gladys," it said. "I want to hear the whole song over again."

George Garrison had not left for Paris after all.

The Glad Rags sang two numbers and were into a third before Garrison stopped them. "All right, that's enough. Alexis, tell Webber I'll be at his meeting in five minutes. Gladys, sit down. The rest of you, wait outside."

Garrison took his overcoat off and gave the coffeepot a shake.

He lit a cigarette. When the others had left, he said: "I take it you have changed your mind. I've been expecting you. I saw that your husband was dead."

Why is it, Gladys thought, that the only men I ever really want to work for are the ones who are either rude to me, or mean, or both?

"Last time I come," she said abruptly (Garrison was off on one of his hikes around the room, his underwear rustling like a duchess in a rage), "you told me I could have a job, but not my sisters or the others in our concert party. Remember?"

"I remember."

"Well, if you still want me, here I am. But if I come to work for you and do all right, will you give my sisters jobs the next time you employ me?"

Garrison swung round. Gladys was not sure (and at that moment, neither was Garrison) whether he was angry or amused. "How old are you?" he asked.

"Thirty-two. Thirty-three in May."

"Thirty-two, and you have the nerve to bargain with me. D'you realize that you are twelve, if not fifteen, years past the age when most artistes come to work for me for the first time?"

"Age don't signify in my case," Gladys said. "Four years ago, you wanted me. If I'm too old for a Garrison show now, I was too old then."

"There are exceptions," Garrison conceded. "But your work is now four years *more stale* than it was. My scouts have been watching you."

Gladys got up. "Then it's high time you got yourself a new set. If your scouts had half an eye between them they'd see that there's no more staleness in my work or in my line of business than there is in yours. How could there be? Our words and music aren't new, I grant you that, but our audiences are—they're fresh to us every time, and it's the audience that matters, whether they're where we play to them, or where you do."

She hasn't failed me, Garrison thought. She's just the way I hoped she might be. Aloud he said: "Gladys, the last time you were here I made you an offer. You refused it. Now I'm going to make you another, but I warn you that if you don't accept—and on my terms—you needn't bother me again."

He sat down at his desk and pressed the fingers of his two hands against each other, a gesture that Gladys was to learn meant that George Garrison was excited. "My new show is only half written and it won't go into rehearsal for a month," he said. "There's work in it for you, and I am also prepared to give a small part each to the girl and the two men who were here with you this morning. Further than that I will not go. As to money, I am prepared to pay the four of you exactly what you are worth to me, and from the way you have been behaving I suspect that that is far more than you imagine." He paused. "And I want your answer now. A straight yes or no."

"Yes."

Garrison jumped up and strode over to the door. "This office is full of people who are paid to put things in writing and answer questions," he said. "Find out who they are and fix everything up before you leave. I don't want to see anything more of you until rehearsals start." Suddenly he grinned, and added: "Good luck! I understand I'm hell to work for."

The reason for Garrison's extraordinary behavior toward the Glad Rags was that in the script of his new revue there was a skit on English seaside entertainment, and the four Glad Rags, seriously playing themselves, appeared to Garrison the best possible casting for it. They had a small beaming pianist who thumped the piano as if it were a drum and bounced up and down while he played; a self-conscious girl with stiff gestures and not at all a bad touch on that ghastly instrument, the concertina; they had a baritone with a face as jovial as a basset hound's and an unpredictably funny woman with the voice of a skylark. There was nothing that Garrison liked better than to offer his critical public a new star, and already this was how he found himself thinking of Gladys Miller. In what way he would use her in the show apart from the pierrot sketch he had not decided, but he found the prospect a pleasing as well as a challenging one. George Garrison was not accustomed to working with artistes of first-rate quality who possessed neither vanity nor personal ambition.

Much later that day, Alexis Brodov said: "*Ça marche*, George."

"What makes you think so?"

"You whistle at the same time as you work."

17

IT TOOK the Glad Rags some while to attend to their necessary business at the Garrison office, but all was settled in time for Gladys, Lily and Tom to catch the three o'clock train home. Cookie was to stay on in London until rehearsals began. Under a sign which said SEASON TICKETS MUST BE SHEWN HERE, Cookie kissed the girls, and said to Gladys: "Take care of yourself, mind. And if there's anything I can do, be sure to let me know."

"I ain't got your address, Cookie."

"Yes, you have. I give it to Blanche. Safer."

The others got into the train, leaving Cookie and Gladys alone on the platform. Gladys said: "It turned out just like you said—we're really up to our necks in gravy now, aren't we? Sometimes I don't know what I'd do without you."

"You *don't?*"

"Well—I mean—"

"Never mind what you mean. Don't spoil it. A fellow can live on a remark like that for weeks."

"I'm not nearly grateful enough for all you do."

"No, you're not. But don't let that worry you. One of these days I shall send in my bill, and then—"

Lily's head appeared suddenly at the carriage window. "Come on, Glad! What does Cookie want?"

"Gladys," Cookie said.

"Well, all right," Lily answered. "But don't make her miss the train."

"Cookie, you're sweet, and I love you, but—"

"How women can ruin things! Why the but?"

"*Gladys.* Quick! Get in!"

"Good-by, Cookie!"

"Good-by, Glad! And God bless. God bless always . . ."

As the train pulled out of Euston Station, through the back streets where, somewhere, Catherine Leake was at work, Lily said: "You were so long with Mr. Garrison this morning, Glad, we got worried. I said to that secretary, 'I do hope my sister isn't wasting Mr. Garrison's time.' She said, 'Mr. Garrison only lets one woman waste his time, and that's the one he's been married to for twenty-seven years.'"

"Oh!" Gladys exclaimed. "That reminds me. I meant to tell them to throw away my red letter."

"We thought of that. At least, Cookie did. You should have seen his face. The girl thought your letter was an advertisement, so it never got put with Mr. Garrison's mail at all. Did you ever!"

Tom, who almost never spoke, said: "What happened today was all your doing, Glad. We owe everything to you."

"I'm sorry they didn't write your contracts up the same as mine though, Tom. I noticed, but I didn't think I'd better mention it."

"I should say not. Seems a lot of money we're to get, doesn't it, compared with the Glad Rags? I suppose it'll cost us more, having to stay in London." Tom turned to Lily. "What d'you suppose your ma-in-law will say when she hears that the present Lady Leake is to appear in a Garrison show?"

"She'll be thrilled," Lily replied, "though she won't be as thrilled as Lady Leake herself. My, Glad, can you believe it—a Garrison show!" Lily always talked too much when she was tired. "Ma doesn't mind publicity for the family if there's money in it. Billy's film company is coming to Tor in the spring to shoot some scenes on Leake Revel's terrace, you know. Ma's as pleased as anything about that. We're going to use the check to help pay off some of the plumbing bills."

While Lily prattled on—partly from genuine excitement, and partly from a wish to keep all of them cheerful—the train sped through the pale daylight of the winter afternoon, and there was time at last for Gladys to think about Fred. With every mile of the journey, it seemed to Gladys that the fascinating world of George Garrison and his revue became less real. What was real was that Fred wouldn't be there in Tor to greet them when they arrived, to smile over her enthralling news, and to ask how soon that Garrison chap would be done with her, so that she could come home for a good long visit? Gladys kept thinking (absurdly) how embarrassed Fred must be to have had to leave them all so abruptly. He had been as particular as Hiram Poole about the small courtesies of life, though dying would not have troubled him. He had never been afraid of death.

It then occurred to Gladys that if, instead of the Glad Rags, she had had Rose Dutton's job at the inn these past years, her father might not have had this heart attack at all. Things never turned out the way you expected them to. Instead of the cottage she had dreamed of as a child, she had lived in rooming houses, and in rented Buena Vista with the laughing clown. And instead of the coal miner with his quiverful of sons, she had had quite different relationships—a sterile, immature marriage, a tedious (though lasting and tender) friendship, an invitation to an evening of adultery in a tiny, cretonned room. The price of glamour, of having, as she had once told Blanche, every day seem like a bouquet of roses, was high, even if one did not include Fred in the account.

The train, a fast one to the North, took them as far as Nottingham. There, they changed to a none-too-clean local, that spent an hour jogging the next twenty-two miles to Manley. At Manley, they learned that the bus to Tor would be late, because a heavy fog blanketed the valley. Tom bought a bag of fish and chips, and the three ate from it while they waited, stamping their feet to keep warm. Tom asked: "How d'you suppose we'll find Mrs. Miller?"

"The same as always," Gladys replied.

18

SHE was, too. She greeted the travelers warmly, setting bowls of hot soup before them at a table in the bar. The Nag's Head had been closed all day. While they ate, Holly asked about their visit to Garrison, and it was not until afterward, when all her family had assembled (the five daughters and the three husbands), that she told them how she had found Fred that morning, apparently asleep in the alcove under the bull's head. "I was waiting for him to come upstairs," she said, "and I must have dropped off, like I do sometimes. We was both very tired. When I woke, I knew it was late. I got up and went out on the landing. The bar lights was still on. I called, and when I got no answer, I went down. I kept calling as I went. Even after I knew what must have happened, I called. Daft, wasn't it?" She paused. "Next thing, I woke Edith, and she telephoned Leake Revel and Mr. Hay. Mr. Hay come at once, and what d'you suppose he did? Made straight for the kitchen and mashed a big pot of tea! Afterward, he prayed." Holly paused again. "I'm telling you all this now because I don't want to have to say it again, and you've the right to know. One night a while back, Fred started talkin' to me about funerals. I wouldn't listen to him, so he went and talked to Mr. Hay. He told Mr. Hay that mournin' over the dead was only fit for pagans, and that when his time came he hoped he'd be treated like a Christian, and that people would feel glad he'd gone where he belonged."

So, because Fred had wished it, the Millers made his funeral service an occasion for thanksgiving. It was a break with Tor tradition, but since Fred had always been careful to conform while he lived, his wishes in death were respected, and even approved of. Fred had never been a man whose opinions were taken lightly. The only person who regretted the change was the undertaker, robbed of an opportunity to display his fancy wares—the hearse with its stenciled plate-glass windows and the four glossy horses in their nodding plumes. No carriage carried Fred to church—his coffin was borne on the shoulders of six friends. As the cortege made its slow, careful journey up the hillside, the rain stopped falling and the sun came out and the bells pealed. The church was crowded, for Fred's customers as well as his friends had come: the service was punctuated by the coughs and creaks that betray the unaccustomed worshiper. They sang "Now Thank We All, Our God!" and the rector read from the Book of Micah: "And what doth the Lord require of thee, but to do justly, and to love mercy, and to walk humbly with thy God?"

That night, The Nag's Head opened as usual, and Holly and her daughters bustled about making everybody feel welcome. A visitor to Tor who did not know the place might have assumed that the innkeeper was around somewhere but that he had just stepped out, which is exactly the way Fred would have liked it.

During the weeks that followed, Holly Miller's behavior startled her daughters. If she had made herself ill with grieving, or refused to consider Gladys' and Lily's impending departure, clinging to them and urging them to stay home with her in Tor, they would have understood her feelings and they might have known what to do about them, but Holly's sorrowing did not take that form. Instead, she became so restless and energetic that her family could not keep up with her. She rose early and she went to bed late, and all day long she ran. She made all sorts of plans for the future and changed them as fast as she put them together. There were, in fact, only two matters on which she was perfectly clear. She wanted to leave The Nag's Head Inn as soon as possible, and she wanted to take a long holiday.

The Miller girls thought their mother had taken leave of her senses. Holly had been born in The Nag's Head, she had always lived there, and so far as they knew, she had never taken a long holiday in her life. But there was no arguing with her. Within a few days of Fred's funeral, Holly had sold The Nag's Head to the Manley Brewery, and accepted an invitation from the Peglers to spend several months with them at Skunby-on-Sea.

"Skunby!" Gladys exclaimed, as though this were the first time she had heard of the place. "What will you *do* there?"

"I thought I might help at Buena Vista," Holly replied at once, making it apparent that she had already planned exactly what she would do. "The old people from the vaudeville that's to have the house, they're moving in soon, and with you having lived there, the place ain't strange to me. It depends of course, but I thought perhaps I might fix 'em up a little bar."

Later, Gladys said to Blanche: "I never expected Mum would be a problem to us, did you? But she is. She's wearin' herself out. All this rushin'! Where's it goin' to end?"

"She'll settle," Blanche replied. "Just give her time. We got to let her face things her own way."

"But going on a holiday, and alone! Mum's always been the one that wanted us to stay together."

"Show some sense, Glad! She still does. Some of us can go with her to Skunby, and while we're there, you can be finding us all a place to live in London."

Blanche took it for granted, as the sisters always did, that wherever Gladys was there would be a home for all of them.

So Holly continued to fly about the inn, packing up and clearing out and throwing things away: the Manley Brewery was to take over on February the twenty-first. Her method was drastic—she disposed of all kinds of treasures that her family had been hoarding for decades—sheet music, pantomime programs, skates, old toys, clothes—even a set of porringers with Peter Rabbit on them. Her behavior distressed Gladys, and only helped to emphasize her feeling that she was living in a deserted, unreal world that contained no Fred, no Benny, no Glad Rags and no Nag's Head Inn.

One Saturday afternoon, Holly's whirlwind progress came to a sudden stop. The cause was none other than the visit of the insurance man, who came this time not to collect money, but to make arrangements for paying it out. From now on, Holly was to receive a weekly pension; not a large sum, but enough for her to live on.

Holly was very quiet during the insurance man's visit. She listened to what he had to say and she signed the papers he brought with him, but when he had gone, she put her head down on the kitchen table and for the first time since Fred's death, she wept. "All these years I complained, and now look what's happened," she said. "I'll never need to go into that home after all now, will I?"

"Home, Mum? What home?"

"The old folks' home in Manley, 'For decayed housekeepers past their labors.'"

"Oh *Mum!*" Her daughters were laughing at her incredulously. "Whatever made you think we'd let you go there?"

"You might a' had to! I wouldn't have taken nothing. Fred and me was always determined we wouldn't take from you children." She dried her eyes, and at once her mind began to flit again. "Glad," she said, "those lovely Glad Rags curtains with the gladioli on 'em. They still at Buena Vista?"

"Yes. Why?"

"They'd make a lovely dress-up for my little bar."

19

GEORGE GARRISON's first rehearsal was called for the last day of the month, one week after The Nag's Head changed hands. Gladys planned to go to Skunby-on-Sea with her mother en route for London, and spend a few days there, clearing up any outstanding Glad Rags business that there might still be. She had already sold the company's costumes and props to the Skunby town council, and

Part V 241

these would presumably be dyed and passed on to the next tenants of the pier theater. Everything had gone except the gladioli curtains: Holly was to have those.

During the days in Tor that remained to them, the Miller sisters kept busy. Three weeks is not very long in which to move out of a village where you have spent your life, though help was forthcoming on every side. Neighbors made pies and roasted chickens and sent them to Holly so that she would not have to cook; Bob Greenhaugh and other friends came in at night and looked after the bar. Homes were found for Fred's rabbits, and his favorite garden plants were dug up and given away. Lily agreed to house Holly's furniture at Leake Revel until she decided where she wanted it to go.

Flo and Blanche were the first of the girls to leave the village. Billy Dyer had gone back to his film studio the day after Fred's funeral, so Flo was very grateful for Blanche's company when she set off to join him—her four children now ranged in age from six and a half years to six months.

Gladys went to Manley to see the party off.

"I'll be coming to London about a week after you," Blanche assured her, "but in the meantime if you hear of a job I could do, let me know and I'll come sooner."

"Perhaps we'll both come," Flo said. "Ask Mr. Garrison when you see him if there's anything in the show for a mother with four good-looking kids."

"If it wasn't for them, he'd probably jump at it," Gladys replied. "Remember how Benny used to say you were the only one of the Millers that had looks *and* talent?"

"Well, I know, but it don't tempt me one bit," Flo said happily. "As I said to Billy, till you've tried it, you don't know what a lark it is to grow up in a family of five."

"*Five?*"

"It's to be Valentine, if the next one's a girl."

Holly and Gladys were to have been the next to leave, while Lily and Tom traveled to London direct from Tor at the end of the month. Cookie had already been commissioned to find rooms for them all. Edith and the twins were to stay at Leake Revel for the time being. These arrangements, apart from the constant changes Holly made—there was an almost daily exchange of post cards between Tor and Skunby-on-Sea—had just been finally settled to Holly's satisfaction when the Garrison office telephoned to say that George Garrison wanted Gladys in London a week ahead of the others.

For some reason this change of plan on someone else's part completely upset Holly. She threw up her hands and could not be reconciled to anything the girls suggested. In the end, since it was too late for a further exchange of post cards with the Peglers, it was decided that Tom and Edith and the twins would go to Skunby with her, since Gladys would not now have time.

There was nothing to be said in favor of these detached, difficult days except that the girls were too busy to think, or to worry. In no time at all February 20 arrived, and with it the departure, on the early morning bus, of Holly and the Holt family. A great crowd of neighbors and friends gathered to see them go, and Holly, in her best hat, smiled and greeted everyone. Tom and Edith loaded the twins and the luggage on board, Gladys hugged her mother, and it seemed immediately after that that the bus was on its way, with Holly and the Holts waving and waving from the conductor's rear platform.

Gladys was to leave for London in the late afternoon. She did not go back to The Nag's Head again. Her luggage (a suitcase and a string bag of apples) were ready packed at Leake Revel, where she spent the morning and ate a not very successful lunch. Lily was tired—she looked as blowsy as only a woman careful of her appearance can look when she relaxes; little Jamie knocked over a jug of milk; and the Dowager told a long story that only she could find funny.

In the afternoon, Gladys paid farewell visits to the Greenhaughs, the Tolmans and the Crews. At each house, tea and little cakes were consumed in the front parlor, the families munching silently. There was, after all, nothing much to say. As Gladys made her way across the green to her last call—the rectory—it began to snow. There was no wind, and the large flakes fell slowly, as if they were a curtain coming down at the end of a play (at the end of a piece of my life, Gladys thought).

In the rectory study, Martin, a log fire, and more tea and cake awaited her. "You realize," Martin said, as she poured for him, "that from now on Tor is going to take a great interest in what goes on in London? Normally we look no farther than Manley, and usually not as far as that."

Gladys laughed. "Don't disappoint me. I like to think that *nothing* in Tor ever changes. I haven't dared look at The Nag's Head since our stuff was moved out, just in case it looks different, even outside."

Martin cut the chocolate cake. "Oh, Tor's changing all the time," he said, "though not fast. Look at Leake Revel, for instance. For the first time in history, a Jamie Leake is being allowed to play on the gibbet steps with the other children when he wants to, instead of being segregated behind his own garden wall. Of course that's your clever sister's doing, but it's change, all the same."

"Well, Leakes has always been funny. I meant everybody else."

"Everybody else is changing too. We're to have compulsory vaccination every time a case of smallpox is diagnosed in the valley."

"Mum always had us done."

"Yes, but then your mother's a sensible woman."

Gladys said: "I'd almost begun to wonder lately if she was! Rushin', rushin', all day long, and sellin' the inn, and goin' away. I can't get over it. It ain't a bit like her."

"She'll be all right. You must let her face things in her own way."

"That's what Blanche said."

"I'm going to miss Blanche, but I'm glad you're taking her with you to London. That reminds me." The rector limped over to a bookcase. He took a small book out of a shelf and blew the dust off it. "Here is something else you can take. A little present."

"A book?" Gladys' voice sounded doubtful.

"Yes, a book. But don't be alarmed, it isn't a book to read. It's by Vermeer—all pictures."

Gladys got up and took her present. "Vermeer? Who's he?"

"A dead Dutchman. You may like to look at him sometimes."

"Thank you very much."

Martin laughed. "What a cockney you've become already! In Tor we don't say thank you. Had you forgotten?"

Gladys said: "Mr. Hay. Suppose I don't do all right down there? We've got no home now, and no money really except Mum's pension and what she got for the inn. We—we seem all cut off."

Martin took her arm and turned her gently around so that she faced the study window. "Look," he said.

There it was, through the richly falling snow, the lovely familiar view—the green, the old gibbet, the ancient church and the cottages huddling together along the lane above The Nag's Head.

"When you go to London," Martin said, "you won't cut that off. You'll take it with you. God gave you your voice direct, but everything else you have has come to you through this village. Your humor, your health, your accent, perhaps even your faith, and certainly the fact that to the end of your days you'll think of damp gray weather as the best weather of all. All that is Tor's forging, and our metal is good. It lasts." He paused, and then added, "Come along now. Time to put on your coat."

He walked with her to the bus stop. It was snowing hard, and no one else except Lily and Jamie Leake had come to see Gladys off. Jamie was carrying her luggage. As the bus came in sight, Gladys was suddenly seized with panic. She felt as if she were emerging from a dream, but that reality was a nightmare. This was not the first time she had experienced panic when Martin Hay was standing beside her. Martin, as producer of the children's Harvest Concerts, had been virtually her first contact with the enthralling, turbulent world of the theater, and he had never been any comfort when she panicked. The frozen heart, the leaden feet—what did he know of them? Years ago, on the night of Hiram's death, he had pushed her onto the stage at Leake Revel and made her sing when singing was the last thing in the world she wanted to do, and now he would do the same thing (only it would be to bundle her into a bus, instead of onto an improvised platform) if she pleaded "I can't go—I was mad to think I could. This village, this valley, is where I belong."

Lily was babbling about luggage. There was snow on Gladys' suitcase. There was snow on everything. Lily was remembering that in theater parlance, snow on one's luggage means that success lies ahead.

I am too old for success now, Gladys' soul cried. I am thirty-two, my father is dead, and I am afraid.

The bus was ready to leave. Lily kissed her. Jamie pumped her hand and shouted, "All the best!"

Gladys turned to Martin. "Seems like the end, don't it?" she said. But when Martin answered, his voice sounded strong, and almost as though a crowd of people, not just one man, was speaking. "Not for you! For you all this—all Tor—is the beginning."

If a shaft of sunlight had reached through the thick clouds and the heavily falling snow, Gladys could not have felt more enlightened: she understood and believed him. I am going to be all right, she thought. Whatever happens, I am going to be all right.

A few seconds later, she left the village. As she looked back from the rear platform while the bus ground its way along the edge of the green past the gibbet steps, she smiled and waved as gaily as Holly had done earlier in the day. She went armed with an old suitcase and a string bag of apples, but to Gladys Miller, formerly of The Nag's Head Inn, they might have been a shining sword, a gleaming buckler.